How to get into
Graduate Entry Medicine

Fifth Edition

Ben Carey

Natasha Morrissey

Dawn Sellars

How to get into Graduate Entry Medicine

Spine Publishing, Dr Prep Ltd, CPC1, Capital Park, Fulbourn,

Cambridge, CB21 5XE

Fifth Edition 2009

British Library Cataloguing in Publication Data

A catalogue record for this book is available from the British Library

ISBN 0-9551325-5-X / 978-0-9551325-5-1

Cover design by Bruce Wilson

Contents

Contributors

Carolin Burchell BSc, MBBS
Doctor

Benjamin Carey MA (Oxon)
Medical Student, Graduate Medicine Course

James Forrer BA Joint Hons, MBBS
Doctor

Berwyck Gibbons
Medical Student, Graduate Medicine Course

Yolande Knight BMedSc, PhD, MBBS
Doctor
Honorary Fellow, Institute of Neurology

Kate McCombe MBBS, MRCP, FRCA
Doctor

Eira Makepeace JP, BA (Rand), MA (Education)
Magistrate
Education Consultant
Director on the UCAS Board of Directors (1995 – 2003)

Natasha Morrissey BSc (Hons), MCSP
Medical Student, Graduate Medicine Course
Physiotherapist

Phyllida Roe BA (Hons), BSc (Hons)
Head of Careers, The Princess Helena College (1987 – 1996)
Medical Student

Dawn Sellars MA (Cantab), MBBS
Doctor
Managing Director, Dr Prep Ltd

Acknowledgements

David Brewis MChem (Oxon)
Schoolmaster, St Paul's School
Company Director, QuizQuizQuiz Ltd

Simon Meller MB BS, DCH, FRCP, FRCPCH, LLB (Hons)
Postgraduate Student in Medical Ethics and Law
Formerly Consultant Paediatrician and Paediatric Oncologist

William Ryder BSc, MSc, PhD
Post Doctoral Scientist

Adam Waldman BSc (Hons), MA, PhD, MBBChir, MRCP, FRCR
Consultant Neuroradiologist, Charing Cross Hospital
Honorary Senior Lecturer, Institute of Neurology, University College
London and Imperial College of Science Technology and Medicine

In compiling a book of this nature we have had to pool information
from myriad sources. Numerous people have helped us in immeasurable
ways. We would like to thank the above people, in addition to

Dr Bishwajit Naha, Dr Bruce Wilson, Dr Pieter Van der Zee, Dr Manoj
Ravindran, Dr Gemma Way, Dr Davina Hensman, Dr Darren Ebreo,
Captain Stephen Penfold, Lucy Kralj, Kate Diamond, Lindsey Wallis,
James and Karen d'Arcy, Caroline Weaver, Shirley Lyle, Joseph Cook,
Derek Brunnen, Amanjeet Dahaley, Ruth Green and our family and
friends.

The Editors

Dawn Sellars graduated from Cambridge University with a degree in Natural Sciences in 1997. She then worked in NHS management before returning to academia with the Institute of Cancer Research. She is a doctor at Frimley Park Hospital, having completed a Graduate Entry Medicine Programme in 2006. She is a trained OSCE examiner for a London Medical School as well as being the managing director of Dr Prep Ltd, a company which specialises in preparing candidates for entry into medical school.

Ben Carey graduated from Oxford with a degree in Biological Sciences in 2003 and then worked in marketing and accountancy for several years. He is now in his final year of a Graduate Entry Medicine Course in London and is experienced in the interviewing and teaching of medical school candidates.

Natasha Morrissey qualified as a physiotherapist in 1997, went on to lead a community therapy team, and gained significant experience in both setting and holding interviews. She has just completed her third year of a Graduate Entry Medicine Programme in London, where she has maintained a position near the top of the class throughout these first three years. She was accepted by all four medical schools to which she applied.

FOREWORD

Why do you want to be a doctor?

Earnest applicants always worry about the 'right' answer to this old chestnut before their interview at medical school. What are they looking for? How can I find out? If the internet has no answer, perhaps I should go to a bookstore or a library. This valuable little book goes a long way to providing some clues.

It was formative experiences in early childhood that directed me toward Medicine as a way of life. My GP was the nicest adult I had ever met, he had miraculous powers and my mother always gave him a cup of tea if he made a house call. At the age of seven, I contracted scarlet fever; at the time the treatment consisted of a month's rest in complete isolation in a fever hospital and, when I was finally released all formites – that is personal belongings which I had touched – had to be incinerated. The reason could never be explained to me, but I now understand that this was because there was no evidence base. "Because the doctor says so" never cut much ice as far as I was concerned, but I was impudently ahead of my time. A desire to question the status quo is a good starting point, but the student needs to understand that it is not what you do, but the way that you do it. A medical school applicant has even less licence to be impudent than the expert patient – even one who is seven years old!

We were successful in a number of medical school entrance exams and interviews, and were fortunate in having backgrounds heavily allied to medicine, in addition to some genuinely inspiring colleagues and friends. We have recognised that many equally capable candidates did not have our fortunate, if not privileged, background. Therefore, we hope to pass on to you the wisdom of those same inspirational colleagues, as well as the knowledge and experience that we have gained through consultation with hundreds of graduate entry applicants to all sixteen graduate entry medical schools. We have tried to construct the content of the book such that the reader can dip in and out of relevant topics where necessary, or peruse it from cover to cover if desired.

This book aims to be a single source of comprehensive information for those considering one of the 16 specific graduate medicine courses. It is written for all graduate entry applicants, whether currently undergraduates, or older applicants with a wealth of life experience. Unlike many 'how to' books for standard entry courses, however, this book is written for the mature thinker. You will not find reference to the cost of a pint of beer anywhere in this book. Conversely, you will find, for instance, a detailed chapter on your future career; something which we (and the medical schools...) rather hope is of concern to you.

Contributions have been made by some insightful and generous colleagues, to whom we are most grateful.

The authors have made every effort to ensure that the information contained within is correct at the time of going to press. Neither the authors nor the editors can be held liable for any mistakes that may have been inadvertently overlooked in the preparation of this book. We take no responsibility for any external sources which we quote.

Why Medicine?

Medicine is the vocation of treating illness and preventing disease. The core of a degree in medicine is the study of the human body, in health and in disease. The range of subjects studied is exciting and demanding. In addition to the study of basic and applied sciences, students will also study public health, statistics, medical ethics and law, practical skills and gain an understanding of different cultures. Whilst absorbing this wealth of knowledge, students will be expected to gain an understanding of the needs of patients and to communicate politely and effectively.

As a medical student and doctor you will need essential qualities such as intelligence and stamina. That said, much of medicine is not rocket science, and some aspects are dull. Patients, however, are uniquely fascinating and an insight into their lives is a privilege.

Medicine is a fascinating and rapidly progressing field and requires its doctors to undertake continuing professional and personal development. There are many career opportunities open to new doctors and a description of what happens after graduation is given in chapter 4. Whatever your chosen career, you will have an exciting and challenging time with highs and lows that are perhaps unsurpassed in other careers.

Medicine is a vocation which requires a strong belief in the value of the path that you are following. It is crucial to understand your own reasons to ensure that it is the right profession for you.

Considering Medicine

If your decision to study medicine is rational and honest not only are you more likely to obtain a place but you are also much more likely to enjoy your chosen career!

We suspect that there are two groups of people reading this. One group of readers are simply considering medicine as a career and would like to know more. The remainder, undoubtedly the vast majority, have already made a firm decision to study medicine and would like to know how to get in. However, interviewers are often left with the feeling that such candidates have simply managed to convince themselves of their desire without holding any true underlying convictions. Think carefully about the following considerations now, instead of during your interview:

Are you being 'pushed' or 'pulled' into medicine? Make sure that you are concentrating on the positive aspects of what is pulling you towards medicine rather than what is making you dissatisfied with your current situation. A push from a current career should serve as nothing more than a catalyst and those candidates who are respectful of their current position tend to be more endearing than those who are derogatory. It can be difficult to determine a candidate's suitability to a medical career when it exists in a cloud of negativity.

Consider the following answer to the question, 'Why medicine?':

'I thought about medicine at school but everyone said I wasn't clever enough. I got straight A's but then it was too late. So I fell into (........*........)   which isn't me. I've tried to stick it out, but I can't imagine doing it for life. No one seems to appreciate me and nothing is ever good enough. I think medicine would be really good.'

This answer is wrong on many levels, and yet the sentiment is frighteningly common. Even good candidates who have a very positive and well researched desire sometimes feel compelled to be defensive and negative too. Describing yourself as someone who dislikes what they are doing, has poor reasons for doing it and even poorer reasons for applying to medicine, is not the way to pursue a career requiring passion and integrity. Few would want this person to be a doctor and such candidates are usually unsuccessful.

For many would-be doctors, another 'push' into medicine is that of pleasing one's family. Distinguishing your needs from those of your family can be difficult when you are younger. A benefit of maturity is the ability to analyse whether pleasing your family will satisfy you throughout your career.

You must identify what is drawing you to medicine. That said, a questionable 'pull' into medicine is that of 'wanting to make a difference'. This statement is obviously not wrong, but it is rather vague and potentially very naive. Everybody wants to make a difference; those that do so have realistic goals. If making a difference for you means breaking bad news in a supportive way, or earning the trust of a frightened child, or motivating a smoker to quit (not forgetting the vast majority of other patients who are not so moved), then making a difference may well be a very good reason to become a doctor. Similarly, if you want to 'save lives' you need to be realistic about what you mean. Doctors save lives every day with prudent use of medicines and surgery but less often with TV-style resuscitation, even when working in Accident and Emergency. For instance, many lives are saved each year by simply measuring blood pressure and treating abnormal values appropriately, which is not most peoples' definition of 'saving lives', yet perhaps it should be.

Another 'pull' into medicine which by itself is insufficient is that of being drawn to it following death or serious illness in one's family. Some have witnessed wonderful care and view those doctors as role models. Others have witnessed unsatisfactory care and seek the opportunity to prevent others from a similar misery. These experiences are valuable, and should in future help that candidate to see 'the heart attack in bed 9' not as a statistic but as someone's beloved father. However, such events can only be the biased background on which you base further research and work experience.

Whist the 'poor' examples for wanting to study medicine given above can be defined, the same is not true for the 'right' reasons, which are unique to the individual. A reason which could be right for one person could be wrong for another. It would also be potentially damaging to attempt to give you 'a right answer' (not least because everyone reading this book might use it!). If your reason(s) for wanting to study medicine are honest, realistic, framed by your skills, and supported with evidence (such as work experience), then you should be the very best person to articulate that personal desire.

Work Experience

Work experience is the only way to even begin to make a decision about studying medicine. The ability to reflect on what you gained from the experience is usually more important than the type of experience itself. It is not essential to shadow respected professors and leaders in their field, whereas it is essential to gain enough 'grass roots' experience to understand what medicine means and how your skills and qualities fit into it. Having a doctor in the family says nothing about whether you will become a good doctor and does not excuse you from gaining work experience.

You need to decide if you can be surrounded by sick and/or needy people. Beyond that, you need to decide if you want to care for them. As a doctor, dealing with patients and their myriad of problems will become your bread and butter, so you need to get a taste for it as early in the process as possible. Can you cope with illness, sadness and death? Can you cope with sadness, hostility (not just from patients), anxiety, complaint and threat of litigation? Are you able to cope with this by virtue of empathy and respect for yourself and others? Do you recognise your limitations? Can you treat as equals those people who take no responsibility for their health? It is human to dislike some people, and patients are no exception, but can you work for them professionally without losing your own fundamentally human qualities? It is impossible to answer these questions without spending some time with the types of people that you will be surrounded by as a doctor.

There are many ways of obtaining decent work experience. Not doing so is rarely excusable, and demonstrates a shallow interest in medicine and a lack of considered investment in your career choice. We have devoted a chapter to various aspects of work experience (see chapter 6).

Who are Tomorrow's Doctors?

It is invaluable to gain some knowledge about the standards expected of future doctors. The duties of a doctor registered with the General Medical Council, as set out in *Good Medical Practice* are:

- *Make the care of your patient your first concern*
- *Protect and promote the health of patients and the public*
- *Provide a good standard of practice and care*
    - *Keep your professional knowledge and skills up to date*
    - *Recognise and work within the limits of your competence*
    - *Work with colleagues in the ways that best serve patients' interests*
- *Treat patients as individuals and respect their dignity*
    - *Treat patients politely and considerately*
    - *Respect patients' right to confidentiality*
- *Work in partnership with patients*
    - *Listen to patients and respond to their concerns and preferences*
    - *Give patients the information they want or need in a way they can understand*
    - *Respect patients' right to reach decisions with you about their treatment and care*
    - *Support patients in caring for themselves to improve and maintain their health*
- *Be honest and open and act with integrity*
    - *Act without delay if you have good reason to believe that you or a colleague may be putting patients at risk*
    - *Never discriminate unfairly against patients or colleagues*
    - *Never abuse your patients' trust in you or the public's trust in the profession.*

The General Medical Council's education committee, which has responsibility in law for promoting high standards of medical education, have produced a series of publications (available online at: http://www.gmc-uk.org/). It is recommended that you read *Tomorrow's Doctors* (1993). This is the cornerstone guidance which has permitted medical schools to introduce new curricula that put the principles of professional practice, as set out in *Good Medical Practice*, at the centre of undergraduate education. Many recommendations are echoed in the medical school prospectuses. Recommendations made in 2003, which replace those published in 1993, further identify the knowledge, skills, attitudes and behaviour expected of new graduates. The emphasis has moved from simply gaining knowledge (indeed, a reduction of the learning burden is recommended) to a greater inclusion of the other essential skills, attitudes and behaviour needed to interact with patients and colleagues.

By way of an example; it is often noted that doctors must have good communication skills. You should not have got this far without having some idea as to why that is important. But what is good communication? As for many skills, the guidance set out in *Tomorrow's Doctors* provides great insight. Can you think of an example from your work experience for each?....

'23. Students must have opportunities to practise communicating in different ways, including spoken, written and electronic methods. There should also be guidance about how to cope in difficult circumstances. Some examples are listed below.

a. Breaking bad news.

b. Dealing with difficult and violent patients.

c. Communicating with people with mental illness, including cases where patients have special difficulties in sharing how they feel and think with doctors.

d. Communicating with and treating patients with severe mental or physical disabilities.

e. Helping vulnerable patients.'

Communication is just one of many skills discussed in detail in *Tomorrow's Doctors*. The document therefore allows you to really think about whether you might have the necessary skills to be a good doctor, to consider your own experiences in context, and to go beyond a simple awareness that certain skills are important. The effect of the GMC guidance shows itself in most medical schools, at all stages from selection, to course design, to assessment.

Schools should ensure that only those who are fit to become doctors are allowed to enter medical school and therefore it stands to reason that they are looking for candidates who at least show the potential to achieve the proposed outcomes of *Tomorrow's Doctors*.

Attitudes toward graduate medical students

As with any fundamental change, some of your future medical colleagues will be less embracing of the newer styles of training. For example, some consultants view the requirement for only essential core knowledge as inappropriate, not least because they had to learn the intricacies of biochemistry and want everyone else to, irrespective of whether it is relevant to patient care. They may also feel that the emphasis on personal development (sometimes rather derogatively referred to as 'fluff') is out of touch with the reality of a busy hospital.

These attitudes are directed at all medical courses that are quite rightly implementing the recommendations of *Tomorrow's Doctors*, but some doctors seem to associate such changes most closely with the graduate entry programmes. In addition to knowledge, a medical student needs to develop interpersonal skills, have maturity, and empathise with both patients and other staff. Where a doctor disputes this, it is probably because he does not possess those qualities himself.

One of the unspoken difficulties of being a mature medical student is accepting adverse treatment from seniors. It is important for all students to know when to accept a situation, and when and how to complain. While being a mature student may make some colleagues' power plays harder to take, your maturity will give you the skills to manage the situation much better than someone who is less experienced.

Special Circumstances

Although special circumstances can relate to both undergraduates and graduates, issues surrounding age and children are more frequently raised within the latter group.

Age

In the United States, medical students must hold a degree before they can enrol. In France, it is very unusual for medical students to be anything but school leavers; an attitude echoed throughout most of Europe. The United Kingdom has an arguably healthy diversity of attitudes towards what is a suitable entry age.

It is difficult to discuss the advantages and disadvantages of being an older student without ostracising the younger candidate (as evidenced by the letters page of the medical student journal, *'The Student BMJ'*). The statements below are simply generalisations; all students are unique and there are certainly many 'mature' students who are anything but. Since a 'mature' student is strictly one that is over 21 years of age, we have tried to use the term 'older' to mean mid to late thirties or so.

Many older students find that learning, particularly rote learning, is far more difficult than when they were in their early twenties. However, graduates have often acquired improved study methods (for example they tend to spend less time colouring-in their notes). Age, and/or a previous degree, enables the individual to identify more easily what they should be learning and to recognise and address deficits in their learning.

Older applicants usually have better communication and social skills in addition to greater life experience. Their ability to see the bigger picture, particularly in a clinical scenario, often surpasses that of their younger colleagues. They often have more financial security, and are likely to be free from the shackles of their previous degree's debt. Attitudes differ towards the value of older students (and graduate courses in general). Indeed, some doctors can be rudely dismissive. The much older student may find that some doctors are highly sceptical of them, but this is undoubtedly balanced by the number who show greater respect.

Medical schools who offer graduate entry degree programmes necessarily value the mature student. Schools are forbidden to discriminate on the basis of age and there is no legal requirement to work for the NHS. But, it is inescapable that the older candidate is unable to serve as many years as their younger counterpart. However, mature students tend to be happier doctors, quickly earn the respect of most of their colleagues, and the quality of their contribution may balance its reduced quantity. With its cost:benefit obsession, these issues are pertinent to the NHS and necessarily important to medical school committees. It can be argued that a quarter of a million pounds of tax payers' money, combined with approximately 10 years minimum training, should preclude those much over 40 years of age.

In practice, candidates over 40 years of age have to be exceptional to be successful. Schools will feel that you have had more opportunity to gain valuable and varied work experience, and to have learnt more from those experiences. You must be realistic and enthusiastic about your career options.

It can be worth consulting the schools themselves, although they are reticent to comment on their notion of suitable age. However, in 2005 a few would still comment:

Birmingham stated: 'We would find it hard to justify accepting any candidate over 40...

Cambridge admissions manual stated: ...candidates should be able to give 25 years' service to the NHS after graduation...

King's College, London stated: 'it is unlikely for an applicant over 40 years of age to be considered and exceptional for an applicant over 45.'

Liverpool stated: 'we do not recommend anyone over the age of 40 applying.'

St George's stated: 'We advise candidates over the age of 35 to seriously consider the implications of starting such a demanding career at this age.'

Warwick stated: 'We do advise that applicants over the age of 30 should carefully consider....

Some medical schools without graduate entry programmes have a particularly open attitude to the mature students. For instance, the University of East Anglia (UEA) in Norwich accepted a 46 year old student - indeed, 57% of the first intake were mature students.

Children

Being a parent does not necessarily preclude you from getting through medical school, as mothers (and fathers) before you will testify. But, there are important practical and emotional factors to consider.

Childcare options include nurseries, childminders, au pairs and nannies, with varying degrees of expense and flexibility. Financial support for childcare is made available to all full-time students by the Dept for Education and Skills (DfES). In terms of nurseries, it may be necessary to secure a place more than a year in advance, which presents a difficult challenge when candidates may be offered a place only months before the commencement of the course. Consider approaching private, council and university nurseries, in addition to the hospital nurseries, although the latter rarely offer places to non-NHS staff. The younger the child, the harder it can be to secure a place.

Depending on childcare arrangements, it may be difficult to commit to out-of-hours work. However, it may be possible to negotiate different on-call schedules. Similarly, some parents have found it easier to secure weekend care for their child, and choose to study then.

Placements at far away district general hospitals also present a potential problem, although some schools are prepared to take this into account for student parents. It is advisable to contact the medical schools directly to find out how far away clinical placements might be and the likelihood of receiving special consideration as a parent and carer.

Socially speaking, 'medical mums' are rarely found propping up the bar in the student union every night - or any night, for that matter. Balancing student life with a circle of mum and baby friends can be hard.

Mothers' coffee mornings are a far cry from student life. A medical mum may feel that she and her child are missing out when friends are taking their babies to Aquatots and the like, but there are many mums who wish they had gone back to work.

Arguably, being a medical mum is no different to being a working mum, apart from the possibility of part-time work; something that a medical degree most certainly is not. A child should not have to miss out; there are plenty of activities at nursery and most mums feel able to make the most of time together. However, medical mums tend to have very well organised schedules, and have a stronger need than most to stick determinedly to their allocated study time.

Disability

Although dyslexia is the most common disability, students with a range of disabilities can successfully gain entry to medical school and complete the course.

Tomorrow's Doctors states: '*... students with a wide range of disabilities or health conditions can achieve the set standards of knowledge, skills, attitudes and behaviour. Each case is different and has to be viewed on its merits. The safety of the public must always take priority.*'

The newly qualified doctor with certain disabilities would find it impossible to carry out some of the clinical tasks normally associated with the first year of practice. For many years, the Medical Act has made special provision for doctors with a lasting physical disability, such that they can obtain alternative and relevant experience.

Summary

- Be realistic about your reasons for being interested in medicine.

- You must be drawn to medicine, not merely disillusioned with your current career.

- Gain sufficient work experience as soon as possible (see chapter 6)

- Read *Tomorrow's Doctors, Good Medical Practice* and *Duties of a Doctor* (www.gmc-uk.org)

- Chose your schools early and double check the entry requirements.

- Prepare for exams early (see chapter 8)

- If you are over 35 years old and/or have children, we would recommend that you discuss your application with your chosen school(s).

Medical Schools

Since 2000, the number of specific graduate entry courses has moved from a single pioneering course at St George's to 16 established courses for entry in 2010. In addition, graduates can enter almost every standard length course in the country; indeed there is no medical school that forbids a graduate to apply to at least one of its courses.

Gaining entry to graduate entry medicine presents every candidate with stiff competition and a diversity of choice. We have compiled core information that will help you to make quick sense of your choices for 2009 entry.

You would be surprised by the number of people who present to interview without showing any level of knowledge about the course to which they are applying. Also, each year there are literally hundreds of wasted applications made by candidates who are not eligible for the course(s) to which they have applied. One would expect more sense from people who consider themselves to be tomorrow's doctors!

You must read the prospectuses in order to make a fully informed choice. There is simply insufficient space to detail all the information which you should know before making your application, and the information detailed here can only be correct at the time of writing.

Admission & Selection

Many candidates try to play the numbers game, and apply to the schools that have the lowest ratio of applicants to places. We have included these numbers here, but note that they do not tell the whole story. Many applicants do not have the academic credentials required and even more do not enter or attend the entrance exams required. Instantly the numbers look better for any applicant. Conversely, there is one medical school that only accepts candidates who hold a first class degree. Simple ratios do not represent the level of competition.

Similarly, candidates often comment on the variable difficulty of entrance exams. This makes little difference to the application, since a difficult exam will be difficult for all candidates, and it is your relative position compared to everyone else that counts. In fact, if many applicants avoid certain entrance exams, believing that they are too tough, the competition will in fact be relatively reduced! Schools have also been known to lower their advertised requirements in light of other qualifications or experience.

Degree class and subject aside, the most important factor for choosing a medical school should be that you like it. There are a number of factors which might be important to you. You need to be willing to live near the medical school for the duration of the course. The course design itself has to be something you are willing to participate in; so you need to decide between a PBL based course versus a traditional one, or something imbetween. Consider also getting a feel for the ethos of the course by trying to meet people on the course, going to open days, and talking to the staff wherever possible. Admissions tutors have repeatedly highlighted to us how useful it is to attend an open day. Places on these can fill very quickly, so we would recommend registering early.

You will need to have a satisfactory health declaration and criminal record check prior to registration for all medical courses. If you have any doubts, we would strongly urge you to contact the medical school; your criminal record check may come through after you commence the course, so failing it would require you to leave immediately.

Standard Entry vs. Graduate Course

Accelerated graduate courses did not exist until the turn of the century, and 16 now exist. Although the courses do not have a long track record, they are based on either existing courses, or on international models, notably those from Australia. There is a great deal of diversity in the forms a course can take, from traditional, lecture based courses, to those based around self-directed learning. There are some that aim to integrate students onto the undergraduate course as early as possible, and others that have a bespoke programme for graduates. Graduate courses may have the following differences in comparison to standard courses:

- Shorter and more intensive
- NHS bursary from years 2-4 (if eligible)
- Greater emphasis on self-directed learning
- Often less preclinical / clinical divide
- Often there are no A-level or GCSE requirements
- Study alongside other graduates

Do not assume that a specific graduate-entry course is necessarily more suitable for you simply because you are a graduate. Much like the choice of medical school, the course you choose should be right for you. Be honest to yourself, as you need to enjoy the years you spend studying. Do you prefer the intensity of a 4 year course, invariably with a greater emphasis on self directed learning, or would you prefer a more traditional lecture based course with longer holidays? Do you like the idea of studying with many school leavers, or is it important that you study only with graduates? Can you afford to reject the extra NHS funding which might be available on a graduate course?

Candidates are not penalised for applying to both standard and graduate courses, and their applications are treated independently. The exceptions to this rule are Swansea and Warwick, for the simple reason that they do not have a standard entry course; Oxford and Imperial, who do not allow candidates to apply for both courses, and King's, whose graduate entry applicants are automatically considered for their standard entry course. Medical schools that accept graduates onto their standard length courses will choose students based on merit, and all deny having a quota.

Course & Teaching Structure

Most graduate courses have an integrated design, where clinical exposure occurs alongside academic study. There are a number of teaching methods associated with graduate courses, and these approaches are being phased into many standard courses. The balance between clinical exposure, problem-based learning tutorials, lectures and special study modules varies from one medical school to another. As graduate entry courses evolve the balance of learning tools will be frequently adjusted. You need to be familiar with the language of medical education:

PBL

In problem based learning (PBL), small groups of students look at the details of a patient's case. Students identify any learning objectives, and use these to direct their learning. As such, PBL facilitates learning in all of the relevant areas, such as anatomy, physiology, pharmacology etc. Alongside this, patient contact, anatomy sessions, and lectures run concurrently to support this process. In contrast to a traditional course, subjects are not studied as academic stand-alone blocks, but instead are looked at as systems in a continually developed and integrated nature, linking to subjects as diverse as law and sociology. Tutorials are chaired by a facilitator, but the emphasis is on self study and reporting back, rather than a formalised teaching session. PBL aims to embed good habits in students, so that when faced with a scenario, they follow a process which will enable them to reason, diagnose and treat correctly. Some medical schools will show prospective students an example of the PBL process in action during their open days. A possible disadvantage to the PBL approach is that the basic sciences, especially anatomy, may not be as rigorously studied.

CBL

Most schools use the term case-based learning (CBL) synonymously with PBL.

Self-directed learning

The emphasis of PBL is on generating learning objectives, studying in your own time, and reporting back. Presenting work to the group is a strong motivator to study. There is some support in the form of lectures, but these can be relatively few. Students are expected to perform the bulk of their learning themselves, using on-line and library resources. Of course, fewer lectures results in free time during the week, making it possible to plan your studies around other commitments, such as having a family or working part-time. The biggest problem with self-directed learning, other than motivating yourself to actually do it, regards the uncertainty about the depth and scope of learning, since it is easy to research too much or skim over important points. As one progresses through the course, the right balance tends to become more obvious.

Traditional Courses

Traditional courses tend to have a greater emphasis on formal teaching, with more lectures, anatomy sessions, seminars, and group discussion. Small group tutorials are nevertheless commonplace, but learning is less likely to be solely built around these than for a PBL focussed course. Traditional courses are more explicit about the level of knowledge that is expected, and tend to cover subjects such as anatomy more robustly. Ultimately, you must decide whether a more didactic approach to learning, with its more structured and regimented experience, will be better for you than an informal, exploratory style of learning.

Amalgamation with standard course

Most graduate entry programmes merge with the standard medical course at some point. This tends to be after a year or two, and the year 'saved' tends to be due to two or three of the standard course years being studied within one or two years. Advantages of subsequent amalgamation are that you will follow a well-trodden route, with a potentially greater understanding of your role and requirements. You will also have a greater understanding of your ranking across the year, which is important as you are likely to be judged against standard course students in the final exams. Joining predominantly younger students is rarely a problem for either group, and will happen upon qualification anyway. However, a system that is unique to the graduate course can lead to novel and efficient schemes that allow greater flexibility. Make sure that you know what type of course you are applying for. Some courses, e.g. Cambridge, will be integrated with the standard course, but expect students to remain in the holidays and make up the rest of the course, whilst others, e.g. Keele, start graduates in the second year of the standard course.

Foundation Courses

Some medical schools offer a 6 year course, normally involving a year of learning basic sciences, enabling students to become proficient to enter the standard course at the normal point of entry. Other courses involve spreading the work of a normal degree over a longer time course, so that the extra science learning is well paced for a student.

The courses widen access to medicine, and tend to be aimed at the less advantaged, or those who lack the basic scientific background needed for medicine. Most accept several candidates per year. The number of students on these courses tends to be smaller. Some courses require some science qualifications whilst others make ineligible those applicants with more than one science A-level or a science degree.

Access to Medicine Courses

These courses are for people who wish to apply to medical schools, but lack the qualifications needed. Students acquire these on a full or part-time basis. There are a limited number of institutions that offer such a course and whilst the course may improve your subsequent application to medical school, please note that many medical schools do not recognise all access to medicine courses. Check with the medical school(s) to which you ultimately want to apply regarding your options. Time may be better spent gaining an AS or A-level in a relevant science.

Patient Contact in the Pre-Clinical Years

Generally, most medical schools will try to get as much interaction between its students and patients as soon as possible. The form that this contact takes varies wildly, but includes sitting in on GPs, following consultants, attending surgery, visiting community programmes, interviewing in out-patients or during a home visit, and goldfish bowl sessions (where a number of students watch treatment sessions from the periphery). The amount of contact varies from school to school, with some ensuring that you have several hours a week from the beginning of the course, to others where you may not see a patient until you start your clinical attachments. Since the motivation of many studying medicine is to meet patients, then it is worth considering what level of contact a course gives you.

Clinical Attachments & Firms

Most courses will have a greater emphasis on clinical attachments as you progress through a course, so that by the last two or three years, the majority of your learning occurs through this method. An 'attachment' refers to a period of time spent attached to a clinical setting, usually a particular department or an entire hospital. The time spent on that attachment is shared with other medical students and is usually dedicated to covering particular themes, for example the clinical attachment for surgery, or for specialties such as ear, nose and throat (ENT). In the UK, the term 'firm' has always been used historically in the clinical setting to refer to the team covering a particular ward, outpatient clinic or clinical section of department. Note that you will also have tutorials and teaching during your clinical years.

Electives

An elective period is one of weeks or months in which the student can choose their own area of study, often abroad, in order to witness and become involved in an aspect of medicine they are particularly interested in or would not otherwise be exposed to. Most students travel to a specialist clinic or hospital. Due to the time constraints of the accelerated courses, some schools are unable to offer an elective period.

Special Study Module (SSM)

In *Tomorrow's Doctors* the GMC recommended the introduction of Special Study Modules (SSM) to widen students' participation in projects or aspects of medicine which might ordinarily be slightly less common or inaccessible, or just to encourage students to take part in an aspect of medicine that is of their own choosing. Medical schools incorporate the SSM period into most years of the course. In some cases the SSM can compulsorily be a research project, while in the later clinical years SSMs can be non-clinical and explore disciplines on the periphery of medicine. To quote *Tomorrow's Doctors*, the SSM is an "...opportunity to study, for example, a language or to undertake a project related to literature or the history of medicine...".

Assessments

Although the assessment strategies for each school are not discussed here, it is useful to understand the terms when reading the prospectuses. Summative assessments are those exams which a student must pass in order to continue their training. Formative assessments often take the same form as the summative assessments but they are set for the students' benefit. Of course, a continuously poor performance in formative assessments should alert the student and staff to the risk of failure such that steps can be taken to raise the candidate's standard for the summative assessments. Medical schools will also use Objective Structured Clinical Examinations (OSCEs) to assess clinical competence, and there may also be written assignments based on other relevant themes, such as ethics and sociology.

Other Factors to consider

Once you have thought about types of course & teaching, there are many other factors that you may need to take into account when choosing where you would like to study.

Big Universities vs. Small Medical Schools

Big universities tend to have more facilities, but there may be an impersonal feel to your experience. There are a number of smaller specialist medical schools, especially in London, whose students read medicine, nursing, physiotherapy and so forth. These tend to have a more friendly feel to them, and are specialised in providing resources for medical education.

Similarly, there are traditional universities where teaching and the way of life are tried and tested but sometimes rather archaic, compared with newer institutions where experimentation is the byword, but without such a track record. Open days are probably the best way of discovering more.

Location of Medical School

Candidates should be aware that there are some medical schools that are not where you would expect them to be! For instance, the graduate course run by Nottingham University is actually located in Derby.

Location of Placements

Many placements are located far from the medical school you are affiliated with. Most are relatively close and should be accessible by public transport, but occasionally they are located far away, and some entail separate accommodation. If you have a family, most schools should ensure that any clinical attachments are convenient for you.

Finance & Accommodation

The financial issues of studying medicine as a graduate are detailed in Chapter 5. Note that several schools can offer financial assistance or scholarships.

Most schools provide University or College accommodation in the first year, with cost depending largely on facilities. The advantages of university accommodation are that it is often cheaper than private accommodation, it may be easier to arrange, especially if the area is unfamiliar, and most schools will house graduates together, so it is a good way of meeting people. Of course, disadvantages include an often poor quality of accommodation, and being back at a Halls of Residence can be noisy and disruptive. Private accommodation prices indicated below are the lowest advertised prices on www.findaproperty.co.uk at the time of writing. Where possible, the prices have been given for one person, based on three sharing.

Admissions statistics and accommodation details relate to 2010 entry and should be used as a guide only. All information is subject to change. You must check any information upon which you are reliant.

The University of Birmingham (BIRM B32) Medicine (Graduate Entry) (4 yrs) (A101) MBChB/Grad

First cohort 2002

Admission and Selection

- Graduates require a 2.1 honours degree in a life sciences discipline. However, to date, Birmingham have only considered candidates with first class degrees. Chemistry equivalent to grade C or better at A-level. Those candidates who have been out of an academic environment for over 3 years need to have worked in a medically related field within the last 2-3 years
- Last year, approx 630 applicants: 80 interviewed: 40 places
- Deferred entry is not encouraged
- Applications from international students are not accepted
- Interviews are held from October – March
- Interviews are structured, and have one of the current students on the panel

Course Structure

- Year 1: CBLs, group work, lectures and primary care. Topics are grouped into four- to six-week themed blocks covering basic science, anatomy (including prosection), ethics, medicine in society and behavioural science, with all these aspects integrated into each of the case studies. Predominantly self-directed learning
- Year 2: Fewer CBLs. Rotations between different teaching trusts Partial amalgamation with third-year students on the 5 year course
- Years 3 & 4: Essentially full amalgamation with the 5 year course
- 6 - 8 week elective period in year 3

Accommodation

- University accommodation: students who placed Birmingham as their first choice are guaranteed accommodation, price range £300-500 pcm depending on facilities
- Private accommodation: From £280 pcm based on 4 sharing

Catchment Area

- National places, but predominantly local
- Accommodation is provided for distant attachments

Proportion of total University student population who are mature students; 11% (2007 figures)

Contact

- www.bham.ac.uk
- Admissions Tutor: Professor Chris Lote; c.j.lote@bham.ac.uk
- Central Admissions: 0121 414 6888
- Medical School Office: 0121 414 3481

University of Bristol (BRISL B78) Medicine Graduate entry (4 years) (A101) MB/ChB

First cohort 2004

Admission and Selection
- Minimum 2:1 in a bio-medical subject. BBB or ABC at A-level including Chemistry (unless included in degree). Candidates should consider at least 4 months' experience as a healthcare assistant or similar
- Last year, approx 452 applicants : 70 interviewed : 19 places
- Deferred entry is considered on a case by case basis
- Applications from students with overseas degrees will not be considered
- Interviews are held from November – end March. Interviews last 10-15 minutes with two members of the Medical Admissions Committee, and are semi-structured. Interviewers will have a copy of the UCAS form in the interview.

Course Structure
- Condensed version of the 5 year MB ChB course with much amalgamation between the two.
- Students on the fast track course will follow the same teaching schedule as the five-year students but will be exempt from the 'Molecular and Cellular Basis of Medicine Unit' and will complete the remainder of the Year 1 & 2 units in one year instead of two. Certain students may be exempt from the Anatomy component of the programme; this will depend on their previous qualifications and is at the discretion of the Faculty under the guidance of the Programme Director

- Integration of clinical experience with core science and extensive tutorial group support. Patient contact begins in phase one of the 1st Year
- This is a traditional style of course, not problem based, with lectures, practicals, small-group teaching and supplemented by self-directed learning and illustrative clinical problems. Anatomy is taught in small groups using prosected cadavers, dissection is optional.
- Clinical teaching is conducted in Clinical Academies.
- 6-8 week elective period
- Bristol has links with other medical schools in Europe, and exchanges are possible

Accommodation
- Accommodation guaranteed for first year only
- Halls accommodation in first year: £188 pcm – £524pcm depending on facilities (2007 prices)
- Private accommodation: From £300 pcm based on 3 sharing

Catchment Area
- Furthest are Gloucester, Swindon, Penzance, all of SE England
- Accommodation is provided for distant attachments

Proportion of total University population who are mature; 7% (2007 figures)

Contact
- www.medici.bris.ac.uk/
- med-admissions@bristol.ac.uk
- 0117 928 7679
- Open days 25th June 2009 and 18th Sept 2009.

University of Cambridge (CAM C05) Cambridge Graduate Course in Medicine (A101) MB/Chir4

First cohort 2001

Admission and Selection

- Minimum 2:1 degree or equivalent, in any discipline
- Plus: GCSE passes at grades A, B or C in: Double Award Science (or 3 single awards in GCSE Biology, Physics & Chemistry) & Mathematics. GCE AS & A-level Passes in 3 of Biology, Chemistry, Physics & Mathematics. One subject must be Chemistry
- Applicants are not required to sit the BMAT unless they wish to use a successful result as part of their pre-medical requirements
- Last year, approx 150 applicants : 75 interviewed : 20-24 places (at Hughes Hall, Lucy Cavendish and Wolfson College)
- Candidates must complete the UCAS application form and a separate application form for the Graduate Course in Medicine
- Applicants may also apply to Oxford University
- Applicants can apply for both A101 and A100 courses, but if you do so, you must apply to the same college (ie Lucy Cavendish or Wolfson. (Hughes Hall accepts graduates only))
- Deferred entry is not permitted
- Applications from international (non-EU) students are not accepted
- Interviews are held in the end of November or start of December
- Interviews consist of a general interview which may include a basic science question, and a shorter interview where the candidate is required to discuss an ethical dilemma which they have been given time to study for a few minutes prior to interview. Interviews are standardised between colleges and are unlikely to have more than 5 members on the panel.

Course Structure
- First 2 years: fully amalgamated with conventional course. Clinical attachments in West Suffolk during the normal university vacations
- After 2 years: integration with much of the conventional course
- The final year is spent in clinical attachments in West Suffolk and at Addenbrooke's Hospital, Cambridge. The emphasis is on integration of primary care, secondary care and the specialties, with encouragement to follow the 'patient journey'
- The main clinical base is in Bury St Edmunds
- Throughout: additional small group work sessions, facilitated by a senior clinician from West Suffolk Hospital, GPs, and the colleges
- Opportunity for a shortened elective

Accommodation
- There is the opportunity to apply for a College Fee Loan (see Chapter 5)
- College accommodation available for 3 years at ~ £300 pcm
- Private accommodation: from £250 pcm based on 3 sharing

Catchment Area
- Bury St Edmunds, Cambridge, Peterborough, Papworth

Proportion of total University population who are mature; 1% (2007 figures)

Contact
- www.cam.ac.uk/admissions/undergraduate
- admissions@cam.ac.uk , 01223 333 308
- Hughes Hall 334897, Lucy Cavendish 330280, Wolfson 335918
- Each college has its own open days.
- General Cambridge Open Days on 2nd and 3rd July 2009

Imperial College of Science, Technology & Medicine (University of London) (IMP I50) Medicine (Graduate Entry) (A101) MBBS/Med

First cohort 2008

Admission and Selection
- Minimum 2:1 honours degree in a biological subject, or a PhD in biological subject
- Your degree must also fulfil a checklist to show it has a breadth of biological understanding– found on website
- An offer is unlikely without relevant work experience
- Candidates are called to interview on the basis of their UKCAT result and all aspects of their UCAS application
- Last year, approx 500 Applicants: 120 interviewed: 50 places
- Deferred applications will not normally be accepted
- Ten places will be available to outstanding overseas students. GCSE English language or IGCSE English as a first language at grade B
- Interviews will be held from late November to mid-January. Interview panels normally consist of a chairperson, two members of the selection panel (medical education staff & clinicians), and frequently a lay observer. Interviews last for 20-25 minutes, and are unstructured. There may be an ethical question, and interviewers have access to the candidate's personal statement.
- Note that if you apply for A101 graduate entry course, you will not be able to apply for the A100 6 year course.

Course Structure
- Course structure is varied, ranging from lectures, group tutorials, practicals, and problem based learning. Dissection used for anatomy teaching.
- The first year is an accelerated learning programme to cover the first 2 years of the undergraduate course, after which students will join the third year of the existing undergraduate course
- At the end of this year, students will then move into the fifth and sixth years of the existing undergraduate course
- Teaching mainly performed at Hammersmith, Chelsea & Westminster, and Charing Cross Hospitals
- 8 week elective period

Accommodation
- First year accommodation £378 – 676 pcm depending on facilities. Note that you will only qualify for university accommodation if you have never lived in a UK university.
- Private Accommodation: from £953 pcm based on 3 sharing (SW7)

Catchment Area
- Mostly inside the M25 for the first 3 years.
- Furthest can be anywhere in the country for the final year, accommodation sometimes provided.

Proportion of total University population who are mature; 12% (2007 figures)

Contact
- www.imperial.ac.uk
- medicine.ug.admissions@imperial.ac.uk
- 020 7594 8056

Keele University (KEELE K12) Medicine (Graduate Fast Track) (A101) MBChB/Grad

First Cohort 2008

Admission and Selection

- Graduates require a 2.1 in an honours degree (any subject, but usually science subjects)
- Achievement within the last two years of a threshold score in GAMSAT
- It is recommended that applicants have work experience in a caring-type role, and be able to describe their experience if required.
- Candidates are called to interview on the basis of their GAMSAT result and all aspects of their UCAS application
- Overall GAMSAT score needed for interview in 2008 was either: 55% average (section I, II and III minimums of 50, 50 and 60) or 60% average (section I, II and III minimums of 50, 50 and 55)
- Last year, approx 150 applicants: only 10 interviewed : 10 places (Surprisingly, about half of last year's applicants were not eligible)
- Deferred entry is permitted
- Applications from international students may be accepted
- Interviews are held in February & March. They are structured and last for 20 minutes, and candidates will be interviewed by 3 people, drawn from the university, hospital and may include a lay person. There are a number of different areas that they will ask you about, and these are listed on their website.

Course Structure

- Students enter directly into year 2 of the standard MBChB course

- Year 1 - 2: Full integration with standard course with extra induction training. Integration of five domains in core systems-based modules in all years with increasing exposure to clinical practice. PBL, lectures & practical sessions. Each week ends with integrating event
- Year 3 - 4: Integrated clinical rotations. Small group clinical problem solving exercises. Students will work in pairs for some placements in non- hospital settings
- 8 week elective period

Accommodation
- College accommodation in first year £243 - 377 pcm
- Private accommodation: from £200 pcm , based on 3 sharing

Catchment Area
University Hospital of North Staffordshire, Shropshire, Staffordshire

Proportion of total University population who are mature; 11% (2007 figures)

Contact
- www.keele.ac.uk
- undergraduate@keele.ac.uk
- 01782 583632/583642/584651
- General open days 14th June 2009 and 23rd August 2009

King's College London (University of London) (KCL K60)
Graduate/Professional Entry Programme (Medicine) (A102)
MBBS/Med

First cohort 2004

Admission and Selection

- Graduates are required to have a 2.1 honours degree or a 2.2 honours degree with a graduate degree (with at least a merit). Any degree subject will be considered. Diploma of Higher Education in Nursing – Pass with at least 2 years nursing work experience. Health Service Professionals with experience may be considered.
- UKCAT is required – normally candidates are selected from those with scores within the top 25% of applicants.
- Candidates are called to interview first on the basis of their UKCAT result, and on other aspects of the application
- Last year, approx 1300 applicants: 160 interviewed: 24 places
- Deferred entry is permitted
- Applications from international students are accepted
- Interviews are held in late January or early February
- Interviews take the form of a Multiple Mini Interview system. Here, interviewees circulate around eight 5 minute stations. At each station, candidates meet one or two interviewers (clinicians) who ask structured questions, and mark independently. In the past, this process has lasted for 30 minutes, and included scenarios and ethical dilemmas, and candidate's personal statements were not seen.
- Interviewed candidates are considered for the A100 standard 5 year course. Usually around 40 graduates are given offers this way. However, graduate applicants can apply to both A102 and A100 if they wish to maximise their chances of studying at King's.

Course Structure
- Throughout the course there is full integration of science and clinical teaching
- Year 1: Separate teaching for the graduate course, at the Guy's Campus. CBL & PBL with clinician or scientist, patient contact, small groups, clinical and practical
- Years 2-4: Students join those of the other MB BS streams for a common course, taught together in small groups of 2 to 8 students, attached to clinically active teams in 'firms'
- 8 week elective period

Accommodation
- First year accommodation from £210 pcm depending on facilities
- Private accommodation: from £412 pcm based on 3 sharing (SE1)

Catchment Area
- South London and locations throughout SE England, includes Kent and Medway

Proportion of total University population who are mature; 19% (2007 figures)

Contact
- www.kcl.ac.uk
- gktadmissions@kcl.ac.uk
- 020 7848 6501/6502
- Medicine open days are fully booked for 2009, but King's also takes part in the University of London Open Days (15th - 16th Sept 2009)

University of Leicester (LEICR L34)   Medicine   (4 years)   (A101) MBChB4

First cohort 2002

Admission and Selection

- 2:1 Honours degree in any discipline.
- Applicants must have significant post-graduate paid employment in a caring role
- Selection for interview is made on the basis of academic excellence, including UK Clinical Aptitude Test (UKCAT) score, along with the personal statement and reference
- Last year, approx 600 applicants: 150 interviewed: 64 places
- Deferred entry is not permitted
- Applications from international students are considered on a case by case basis in writing
- Interviews are held in November – March
- The interview lasts about 20 minutes and is with a senior academic or doctor and a 5th year medical student. Interviews are semi-structured, and will judge characteristics such as communication ability, motivation and suitability. Interviewers will not have access to the candidate's personal statement

Course Structure
- Condensed version of the 5-year course. Teaching is a mixture of small group based problem solving and traditional teaching.
- First 1.5 years: Separate course for graduate entry. Integrated system based course with early patient contact
- Year 1.5 - 4: fully amalgamated with standard entry course
- Integrated clinical and medical science throughout
- Small groups, clinically related problems, some lectures
- There is the opportunity for an elective period of study

Accommodation
- College accommodation guaranteed in first year £250 - £500 pcm depending on facilities.
- Private accommodation: from £238 pcm based on 3 sharing

Catchment area
- Generally based in Leicester
- Furthest placements are: Kettering, Boston, Peterborough

Proportion of total University population who are mature; 14% (2007 figures)

Contact
- www.le.ac.uk/sm/le
- med-admis@le.ac.uk
- 0116 252 2969/2985
- Medicine Open Day Saturday 20 June 2009, with other general open days later in the year.

The University of Liverpool (LVRPL L41)   Medicine (Graduate Entry) (A101) MBChB/Grad

First cohort 2003

Admission and Selection
- Minimum 2:1 in a Biological, Biomedical/Health Science degree plus a minimum of ABB at A-level including Biology and Chemistry (at least one at A grade) and an additional B grade for AS-level. Note that applicants must already have their degree at time of application
- You must also demonstrate appropriate healthcare experience
- Selection is based on academic and non-academic requirements
- Last year, approx 400 applicants : 50 interviewed : 32 places
- Deferred entry is not permitted
- Applications from international students are not accepted.
- Interviews are held between late November - March
- 15 minute interview

Course Structure
- Year 1: Condensed version of years one and two of the 5 five-year programme. PBLs, some lectures, weekly clinical skills training and early clinical contact in hospitals and the community
- Year 2: Full amalgamation with years 3-5 of standard course, with PBLs and clinical sessions
- 5 week elective period

Accommodation

- College first year accommodation provided at £316 – 450 pcm depending on facilities
- Private accommodation: from £230 pcm based on 3 sharing

Catchment Area

Furthest are:

- Barrow-in-Furness, Kendal, Lancaster

Proportion of total University population who are mature; 18% (2007 figures)

Contact

- www.liv.ac.uk
- mbchb@liv.ac.uk
- 0151 794 2000
- 0151 706 4266
- Open days are in September & June
- General University Open Days on 27th June 2009 & 27th Sept 2009.

Newcastle University (NEWC N21) Medicine (Accelerated Programme, Graduate Entry) (A101) MBBS/Acc

First cohort 2002

Admission and Selection

- Minimum 2:1 Honours degree in any discipline. Also health care professionals with a qualification recognised by a statutory body, who have relevant experience which includes a substantial amount of contact with patients gained within the NHS or equivalent body.
- Applicants are required to sit the UK Clinical Aptitude Test (UKCAT)
- Applicants are expected to show evidence of academic endeavour within the last 2-3 years & experience in a caring environment.
- Candidates are considered for interview on the basis of their application form and UKCAT scores
- Last year, approx 800 applicants: 150 interviewed: 30 places
- Deferred entry is permitted
- Applications from international students are not accepted
- Interviews are held in November - March. Interviews are conducted by two selectors (normally 1 will be a clinician); each will grade candidates on basis of personal statement, reference and contribution at interview. It is a semi-structured interview, where discussion is allowed. Interviewers have access to the candidate's personal statement.

Course Structure

- Emphasis on PBL, and contact with patients occurs throughout the course. Prosection is used to teach anatomy

- Year 1: Independent from standard course. Integrated clinical and core science. CBLs are with a senior medical tutor. Teaching and learning is centred around small study groups and is structured around the core subject areas covered in Phase I of the five-year course (minus the student-selected topic)
- Year 2-4: Full amalgamation with 5 year course: Some time based in one of four regional Clinical Base Units. Also a 12 week course in clinical sciences and investigative medicine, followed by a 30-week period of student-selected components and elective study
- 8 week elective period
- Opportunity for a 1 year intercalated BSc

Accommodation
- Probable college accommodation in first year; £244 - 412 pcm depending on facilities (2007 figures)
- Private accommodation: from £260 pcm based on 3 sharing

Catchment Area
- Tyne, Wear, Northumbria, Tees, Middlesborough

Proportion of total University student population who are mature students; 9%

Contact
- www.ncl.ac.uk
- mbbs.admissions@ncl.ac.uk
- 0191 2227005
- Specific medicine open days only offered to applicants that have been successful in gaining an offer. General open days are available.

The University of Nottingham (NOTTM N84) Medicine (Graduate Entry) (A101) BMBS/Med

First year course ran: 2003

Admission and Selection
- 2:2 degree in any subject (or a higher degree (Masters or PhD) in lieu of a first degree) and a competitive score in the GAMSAT examination (62% for entry in 2005, 62% for 2006, 61% for 2007, 60% for 2008, 58% for 2009)
- Based in Derby
- Emphasis on long-term appropriate work experience
- Last year, approx 1000 applicants: 300 interviewed: 90 places
- Deferred entry is not permitted
- Applications from international students are accepted from 2009
- Interviews will be held in 22 - 26 March and 12 - 16 April 2010
- Interviews are highly structured. The structure does not allow for interactive discussion. They last for 30-40 minutes, and there are 3 members of the interview panel (an academic, a clinician & a lay person). Interviewers will not have access to a candidate's personal statement.

Course Structure
- First 18 months: based in a new purpose-built medical school building on the Derby City Hospital campus. PBL with a trained facilitator, early clinical experience, small-group teaching, lectures and workshops
- 18 months – 24 months: Full amalgamation with the five-year course with the same modules/attachments in a variety of clinical sites in the mid-Trent region. Modules in Clinical Practice (Medicine &

Surgery) and Community follow-up, Infection, and Therapeutics. Small-group teaching by specialists and attachments to clinical firms.

- Last 2 years: 10 weeks Obstetrics and Gynaecology, 10 weeks Child Health, 10 weeks Health Care of the Elderly and Psychiatry, 10 weeks Ophthalmology, Ear, nose and throat, Dermatology and a Special Study Module. Advanced Clinical Experience and shadowing
- 9 week elective period

Accommodation
- College accommodation in first year from £260 pcm in Derby
- Private accommodation: from £135 pcm (Derby), based on 3 sharing

Catchment Area
- Trent area, Derby, Nottingham, Lincoln, Mansfield

Proportion of total University student population who are mature students; 7% (2007 figures)

Contact
- www.nottingham.ac.uk
- GEM@nottingham.ac.uk
- 01332 724622
- Open Days 28th April 2009, 13th May 2009 and 6th June 2009.

Oxford University (OXF O33) Medicine (Fast-track, Graduate Entry only) (A101) BMBCh4

First cohort 2003

Admission and Selection

- 2:1 degree in applied/experimental science & A-level Chemistry (unless component of degree) & one other science A-level
- All applicants are required to take the UKCAT entrance test
- Work experience is useful but not a pre-requisite
- Candidates must complete the UCAS application form & the Oxford Application Form including a short statement and 3 references, preferably academic, by 15th October.
- Shortlisting for interview is based on the UKCAT, the application form, references & personal statement
- Students would have a low chance of success if scoring less than 600 for each section and may need much greater scores for consideration
- Applicants to the graduate course may not apply to the conventional 6 year course at Oxford, but they may apply to Cambridge
- Last year, approx 250 applicants : 90 interviewed : 30 places
- Deferred entry is not encouraged, but is possible
- Applications from international students are accepted.
- Interviews are held in December, and include an academic component. Different colleges use different interviewing processes, generally using three consecutive interviews. Interviewers are blind to your UKCAT score but not your personal statement

Course Structure

- Year 1: Basic sciences taught within a clinical context (greater clinical emphasis in year 2). Problem-oriented seminars with specialist

tutors, held after independent study of that topic. Very few lectures. Highly self-directed, supported by college tutorials of two or three students. One day a week spent learning clinical skills, with additional tutorials on clinical skills of 2 or 3 students
- Year 2: Largely merged with the first year of clinical study on the conventional course
- Years 3&4: Full amalgamation with standard entry course
- 10 week elective and other opportunities to go abroad

Accommodation & College Fees
- Oxford colleges charge a fee of £5000 to £6200 pa in addition to the tuition fee in the first year only. Note that you may be eligible for a College Fee Loan (see Chapter 5).
- Accomodation in Year 1: varies by college but averages £3,200 p.a.
- Year 2 onwards: Nearly all students live in private accommodation: from £300 pcm, based on 3 sharing

Catchment Area
- Year 1: clinical days (one pw) are almost entirely run in Milton Keynes and GPs surgeries in Buckinghamshire; transport is provided
- Year 2-4: Furthest are Milton Keynes, Banbury, Northampton. Short overseas options in yr 3 (e.g. Sri Lanka, New Zealand, Australia)

Proportion of University student population who are mature students; 17%

Contact
- http://bmra.pharm.ox.ac.uk
- undergraduate.admissions@admin.ox.ac.uk
- 01865 270211
- Open days roughly every 3 months, including July 17th 2009

Queen Mary, University of London (QMUL Q50)   **Medicine**
(Graduate Entry) (A101) MBBS/Grad

First Cohort 2003

Admission and Selection

- 2:1 honours in a science or health related degree. A Master's degree may be considered if it is undertaken as part of the first degree. only your first degree will be considered for selection purposes, and must contain significant Chemistry and Biology (a requirement which may be offset by A-levels)
- Last year, approx 1000 applicants: 150 interviewed: 40 places
- NB. 10 places are reserved for Queen Mary's Biomedical Sciences graduates & other medically-related courses at Queen Mary.
- Selection criteria for interview are based on showing a commitment to medicine in the personal statement, a satisfactory reference, and a high UKCAT score.
- For 2009 entry, applicants with scores above 2450 were considered.
- Candidates are recommended to have performed work experience.
- Deferred entry is not permitted.
- Applications from international students are accepted (~5 places)
- Interview conducted in association with Warwick University.
- Interviews are usually held in March. Interview structure varies year on year, but are assessment centre formats and have included in the past such tests as critique of a video of a doctor-patient consultation, team tasks and ethical dilemmas. There will also be a structured interview. The process takes around 4½ hours

Course Structure
- Year 1: The course runs jointly with City University as a multi-professional course, where medical and dental students join an equal number of graduates who are on accelerated courses leading to qualifications in nursing. PBLs taught by professionals, and medical topics integrated into systems that cover a core curriculum.
- Year 2: PBL and continued inter-professional learning. Amalgamation with third year undergraduate students for integrated clinical studies in general practices and on the wards of associated teaching hospitals.
- Year 3 & 4: Significant amalgamation with standard programme including exposure to the specialties and shadowing.
- 12 week elective period

Accommodation
- First year accommodation £280 - £503 pcm at the Barts site
- Private accommodation: from £390 pcm based on 3 sharing (E3)

Catchment Area
Furthest are: Southend, Chelmsford

Proportion of total University student population who are mature students; 21% (2007 figures)

Contact
www.qmul.ac.uk
www.smd.qmul.ac.uk
gepmedicine@qmul.ac.uk
0207 8822244
Graduate Entry Medicine Open Day 15th July 2009.

University of Southampton (SOTON S27) Medicine - Graduate entry (4 year) (A101) BM4/Med

First Cohort 2004

Admission and Selection

- 2.1 honours degree in any subject and either pass grade at A-level Chemistry or AS-level Chemistry and Biology/Human Biology
- UKCAT is required
- Graduate applicants are not normally interviewed but graded on academic and non-academic criteria
- Last year, approx 1600 applicants : 0 interviewed: 46 places
- Deferred entry is permitted
- Applications from international students are accepted

Course Structure

- Years 1 & 2: Small group work structured around clinical topics. Substantial clinical experience, and amalgamation with the 5 year programme for some lectures and practicals. Students have 2-3 clinical sessions each week in both hospital and community settings. Dedicated clinical teaching staff for clinical work in Winchester. Prosection used to teach anatomy.
- Years 3 & 4: Similar programme to the 5 year programme
- Clinical work is undertaken at the outset, in a dedicated hospital base
- No opportunity for electives

Accommodation

- First year guaranteed; £270 – 557 pcm depending on facilities (2007)
- Private accommodation: from £70 pcm based on 3 sharing

Catchment Area

- Includes: Portsmouth, Winchester, Southampton, Salisbury

Proportion of total University student population who are mature students; 20% (2007 Figures)

Contact

- www.som.soton.ac.uk
- aj2@soton.ac.uk
- 023 8059 4408
- Open Days 3rd July 2009, 4th Sept 2009, 5th Sept 2009

St George's, University of London (SGEO S49) Medicine (4-year Graduate Entry) (A101) MBBS4

First Cohort 2000

Admission and Selection

- 2:2 honours degree in any discipline or a higher degree such as MSc, MA, MPhil or PhD. Candidates are called to interview on the basis of their GAMSAT result (62% for entry in 2006, 61% for 2007, 55% for 2008, 56% for 2009)
- Only 1102 of the 1423 applicants attended GAMSAT exam in 2007
- No GCSE or A Level requirements
- Applicants are required to have relevant work experience, and there is a scoring system that rewards greater experience
- Last year, approx 740 applicants: 320 interviewed: 112 places
- Deferred entry is permitted
- Applications from international students are not accepted
- Interviews will be held in January
- Interviews are highly structured. The structure does not allow for interactive discussion. Interviews last for 40 minutes, and cover the full range of qualities expected of a doctor. The interview panel consists of three people, including a medical student. This may soon be replaced by a Multi Mini Interview assessement (see King's)

Course Structure

- Year 1: Scientific, ethical, statistical & epidemiology themes are learnt through PBL, lectures, dissection led anatomy sessions & clinical skills. Integration of clinical teaching and core science. Early clinical contact throughout the year, and the emphasis is on self directed learning and maximising patient contact.

- Year 2: This year is divided into blocks, 6 weeks in duration. Students will rotate through these blocks, as in Year 1. These blocks are split with 3 clinical attachment blocks, including Primary Care, Geriatrics and General Medicine/Surgery.
- Year 3: Students rotate around seven 6 week clinical placements, including General Medicine & General Surgery, along with Paediatrics, Psychiatry, Neurology, and Obstetrics & Gynaecology.
- Year 4: Acts as training for life as a F1 Doctor, rotating through General Practice, A&E, and being attached to 2 hospital firms in medicine and surgery.
- 10 week elective
- Other 'mini-electives' and SSMs allowing for study abroad. Swap possible with Flinder's university in Australia in Year 3.

Accommodation
- First year new college accommodation provided at £403 pcm
- Private accommodation: from £303 pcm based on 3 sharing

Catchment Area
Mostly SW Thames region, but can be as far as:
- Liverpool, Isle of Wight, Plymouth, Yeovil, Darlington

Proportion of total University population who are mature; 40% (2007 figures)

Contact
- www.sgul.ac.uk
- gep@sgul.ac.uk
- 020 8725 5201
- Open Days 3rd June 2009 and 9th Sept 2009

University of Wales Swansea (SWAN S93)   Medicine (A101) MBBCh/Med

First Cohort 2004.

Admission and Selection
- Swansea only offers a graduate-entry programme
- 2:1 in any degree with some post-GCSE experience in Biology or Chemistry desirable
- Candidates are required to sit GAMSAT.
- Interview selection is based on Personal Statement, academic achievement, and GAMSAT score
- Candidates with scores less than 50% are very unlikely to be successful
- Last year, approx 600 applicants : 220 interviewed: 70 places
- Deferred entry is not permitted
- Applications from international students are not accepted
- Interviews are held in the last 3 weeks in January. Interviews last for 30 minutes, and are semi-structured. The panel consists of two members – usually a clinician and a non-clinician. Interviewers will have access to a candidate's personal statement.

Course Structure
- Years 1 & 2: Equivalent programme of study to the first 3 years of the Cardiff medical course. Case based learning. Integration of science and clinical medicine throughout
- Years 3 & 4: Clinical training with teaching
  All study is based in Swansea (until 2009 the final 2 years were based in Cardiff)
- 6-8 week Elective

Accommodation
- First year college accommodation: from £238 pcm. Located a 10 minute drive from campus.
- Private accommodation: from £238 pcm (Swansea University figures)

Catchment Area
All-Wales Clinical Training Rotation. The furthest are:
- Bangor, Wrexham

Proportion of total University student population who are mature students; 18% (2007 figures)

Contact
- www.gemedicine.swan.ac.uk
- medicine@swansea.ac.uk
- 01792 602618
- Open Days 24th June 2009 and others later in the year.

The University of Warwick (WARWK W20)   Medicine   MBChB (A101) MBChB/4

First Cohort 2000

Admission and Selection
- 2:1 degree in the Biological, Physical or Natural Sciences or certain Health Science degrees with practical experience. Will allow a 2:2 with appropriate PhD.
- Warwick only offers a graduate-entry programme
- Applicants are required to sit UKCAT – minimum of 50th centile
- Candidates must have work experience in different healthcare settings, and have learnt from their experience
- Selection for interview is based on UKCAT results & UCAS form
- Last year, approx 1500 applicants: 400 interviewed: 178 places
- Deferred entry is not permitted
- Applications from international students are accepted – there are 14 places available
- Selection centres are held in conjunction with QMUL on 22-25 March 2010
- Selection centres in the past have included: A written exercise, viewing a video consultation, an interview, a teamwork exercise and completion of a Questionnaire. The process takes 4½ hours.

Course Structure
- The course is a condensed version of the 5 year course at Leicester and removes those elements which graduates in the biological sciences are expected to have studied in depth
- The course itself consists of case based discussion in group work and moves onto more self-directed learning

- Phase 1 is for the first 18 months involves lectures, with case-based discussion in groups, clinical skills.
- Phase 2 is a series of 8 week rotations with 2 students allocated to a pair of consultants for each rotation.
- Contact with patients starts from the first semester in Phase 1
- Plastinated models are used for anatomy teaching
- 6 week elective period at end of third year

Accommodation
- First year accommodation from £355 pcm on campus depending on facilities. Also off-campus accommodation available
- Private accommodation: from £240 pcm based on 3 sharing

Catchment Area
Clinical attachments are across all sites utilised by the Warwick Medical School:
- UHCW NHS Trust (Walsgrave), George Eliot (Nuneaton), The Alexandra Hospital Redditch, Warwick Hospital.

Proportion of total University student population who are mature students; 30% (2007 figures)

Contact
- www2.warwick.ac.uk
- pgteam4@warwick.ac.uk
- 024 765 74550
- 024 765 28101
- Open days in September, February & June. For further dates please refer to the website

	First Cohort	Degree	Subject	Exam	No. Apply	No. Interviews	No. Places
B'ham	2002	2:1 (1st)	Science		630	80	40
Bristol	2004	2:1	Science		452	70	19
Cambridge	2001	2:1	Any	(BMAT)	150	75	22
Imperial	2008	2:1	Science	UKCAT	500	120	50
Keele	2008	2:1	Any	GAMSAT	150	10	10
King's	2004	2:1 or 2:2+PhD	Any	UKCAT	1300	160	24
Leicester	2002	2:1	Any	UKCAT	600	150	64
Liverpool	2003	2:1	Science		400	50	32
Newcastle	2002	2:1	Any	UKCAT	800	150	30
Nott'ham	2003	2:2	Any	GAMSAT	1000	300	90
Oxford	2003	2:1	Science	UKCAT	250	90	30
Queen's	2003	2:1	Science	UKCAT	1000	150	40
S'hampton	2004	2:1	Any	UKCAT	1600	0	46
George's	2000	2:2	Any	GAMSAT	740	320	112
Swansea	2004	2:1	Any	GAMSAT	600	220	70
Warwick	2000	2:1	Science	UKCAT	1500	400	178

Summary

- Entry requirements aside, you should pick schools which you like
- We can only include basic outline information here
- Do not be mislead by an apparently 'easier' application process. A mere ratio of applicants to places does not determine the standard of the competition
- Study the prospectuses carefully
- Become familiar with the different teaching methods and facilities available at each school
- Attend Open Days
- Make your decision early to allow time for exam and interview

A Medical Career

Securing a place on the graduate entry programme will be foremost in the mind of any applicant, but of course if you succeed, and pass all of the exams, what can be expected following graduation?

In practice, completing the MBBS course is as much a licence to train further as it is a qualification in itself. The course will finish in June and on the first Wednesday of August you will begin work as a Foundation year 1 doctor (F1 / FY1). This marks the beginning of junior doctor training, a programme of education and assessment that could lead to a specialist training post.

Post-graduate training has changed and a new structure called 'run through training', (designed for the Modernising Medical Careers (MMC) programme) was introduced on August 1st, 2007. The original version of the training programme is represented diagrammatically below. The aim is to provide 'seamless training' of doctors from the moment they leave medical school to the time they finish their training. Entry into the programme is competitive and open to those doctors who have successfully completed foundation year 2.

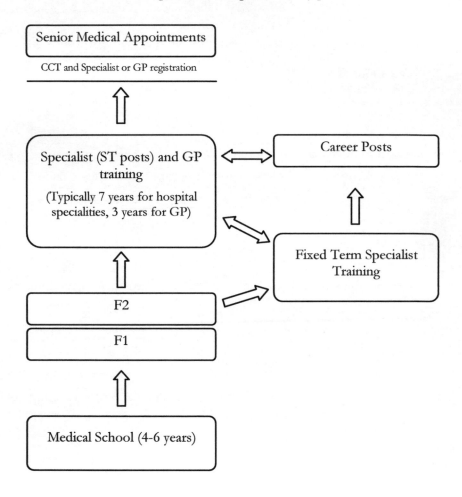

UK Modernising Medical Careers (MMC) Original Framework Proposal (2007)
Arrows represent a competitive entry process

Senior Medical Appointments

CCT and Specialist or GP registration

Specialist (ST posts) and GP training

(Typically 7 years for hospital specialities, 3 years for GP)

Career Posts

F2

F1

Fixed Term Specialist Training

Medical School (4-6 years)

The General Medical Council (GMC)

The GMC, an independent charity registered organisation, is responsible, by statute, for regulating doctors to ensure good medical practice. All UK graduates are eligible to be on the GMC's register and all doctors must be registered with the GMC in order to practise in the UK. As an F1 doctor, 'provisional registration' will cost you £140 and upon satisfactory completion of the F1 year, your registration will be upgraded to 'full'. Each August thereafter, you will have to pay an annual retention fee of £410.

Application to Foundation Programmes

Since 2006, application to the Foundation Programmes (years 1 and 2) has been made via a centralised computer system (similar to UCAS). Post graduate training is now run at a regional level by newly formed Foundation Schools. A Foundation School brings together medical schools, the local deanery, trusts (acute, mental health and PCTs), and other organisations (e.g. hospices) in a particular geographical area, to offer foundation doctors in training a range of different settings and clinical environments. UK graduates are eligible to apply to any Foundation School they chose by filling in a single on line application form, which is then scored centrally. At the time application you will be asked to rank the Foundation Schools in your order of preference. All candidates applying to a particular school are then ranked and offers of employment are made accordingly, without interview. Your application to a Foundation School is made centrally and you will receive one offer only. The Foundation School itself will then allocate you one Foundation Programme. If you refuse either the school or the programme, you will have to withdraw from that year's application process; there is no 'clearing' system.

The structure and content of your foundation years will depend on the deanery to which you apply. Some will accept you onto a 2 year programme, and the specialties through which you rotate will be predetermined. Others will only allocate specialties for the first of the two years such that, six to eight months into your first year, you will apply for the specialities in which you wish to work in your second year. This is likely to be a competitive process as some posts are more popular than others and places will be limited.

Foundation Years

The Foundation programme has replaced the old pre-registration house officer (PRHO) year and it is intended to better bridge the gap between medical school and specialist or GP training. Information about the programme is available on the website, www.foundationprogramme.nhs.uk.

All F1s must work for at least three months in each of a medical and surgical specialty during the year. The Foundation programme has moved away from the traditional six months of each medicine and surgery to introduce trainees to a broader range of career options. Hence specialties such as chemical pathology, microbiology, public health, paediatrics, anaesthetics, intensive care, psychiatry, obstetrics and gynaecology and are available during the first year. General practice is not offered until the F2 year.

Even though the structure of training has changed, the day to day job remains mostly the same. Each day you will be involved in some form of 'ward round', during which you review the on-going condition and management of patients who are in hospital under the care of your consultant. This is led by your consultant twice a week, on average, and on other days it is led by the firm's Specialist Trainee or Registrar. The ward round generates jobs for the rest of your day, e.g. ensuring tests and investigations are ordered, performed and reported upon and referrals to other specialties or centres are made. At the end of each day the F1 updates the list of patients, collates the blood results, generally tidies up any loose ends and informs the on call team of any patients who may be a cause for concern over night.

Usually at least one day of each week will be the "on take" or "on call" for your team; most patients presenting acutely to the hospital in that time will be admitted under the care of your team. This on take period may last twelve hours (either day or night), twenty four hours, a weekend or in some surgical specialties, a whole week. Although patients admitted during this time will ultimately be under the care of your team, you will not necessarily be at work for the whole time. Twenty four hour on call shifts are a thing of the past, and the maximum allowed nowadays is 13 hours, in line with the European Working Time Directive (EWTD). However, whilst on call, your team are ultimately responsible for clerking and instigating management of new admissions, reviewing in-patients whose conditions have deteriorated, etc. As a junior, you should always have senior support available.

Other events in your average week may include protected teaching sessions, meetings e.g. radiology meetings, multidisciplinary meetings (i.e. discussions with e.g. physiotherapists, occupational therapists, dieticians about specific patients) and you may be asked to present interesting cases at departmental meetings. During your surgical job you may be expected to conduct pre-operative assessment clinics where you assess patients' fitness for surgery. Your aim is to highlight any problems which may delay or prevent surgery and organise further investigation or treatment as necessary.

In amongst all this, there should be time to support the hospital social life and let off steam at the institution (and some would say Rite of Passage) that is the Doctors' Mess Party!

Assessment

Your progress through the foundation years will be recorded by you in a Personal Development Portfolio. Much emphasis is now placed on assessment and demonstrating competency. The assessments take a variety of forms including:

- Self evaluation
- Assessment by up to 12 doctors and nurses on performance and attitudes.
- Direct observation and assessment of your interaction with patients in a variety of clinical problems
- Direct observation and assessment of practical skills
- Case presentations and discussions

You will also be expected to:
- Produce further evidence to show that you have met the objectives of the F1 curriculum
- Reflect on your own practice, the impact of the job on you and on your coping strategies. NB. Self evaluation and the ability to reflect on one's practice is an attribute that is now not infrequently tested at medical school interviews.

Essentially, these assessments formalise the process of training which has gone on quietly for centuries. None of these processes is new, but in this era of accountability, competency has to be proved and documented and is no longer assumed.

Foundation Year Two

The second year follows a very similar structure to the F1 year, with four months being spent in three different specialties. This year allows you to take more responsibility and to see patients in specialty clinics. You will also be responsible for supervising your F1, should you have one. There is an emphasis on becoming an "emergency-safe doctor" and many of the available Foundation Year 2 posts include placement in accident and emergency. At the end of F2 you will receive a Foundation Achievement of Competency Document (FACD) and be eligible to apply to specialist training in your chosen field.

Modernising Medical Careers and Specialist Training Application

Application to Specialist Training Programmes is now made via a single on line application form. For the vast majority of specialties, this form is then sent to your chosen deaneries and the process of selection is managed at deanery level. A very few specialties have opted for a centralised, national recruitment system. The original training programme is represented diagrammatically at the start of this chapter. There have been a few changes to this programme in certain specialties that have 'uncoupled' their 'run through' training progammes. This means that successful application to specialist training secures you two years of 'core training' (CT1 and 2) only. After this, you must apply again in an openly competitive process to secure your ongoing career progression as a Specialist Trainee (ST3 – 7). Details of the each specialties' programme can be found on the website www.mmc.nhs.uk.

A cynic might suggest that this 'uncoupling of the seamless run through programme' is a little like reinventing the wheel…

Training can end in one of two ways; either by moving through the training scheme to achieve a Certificate of Completion of Training (CCT), or GP registration, which entitles doctors to apply for Consultant posts or substantive GP posts respectively; or by choosing to leave training and take up a Career Post, a position referred to as a Staff Grade in the old system. People in these posts are not 'in training' and are employed for service provision.

The run through training, as with the foundation years, will be 'competency based'.

Running alongside the Specialist Training programmes will be Fixed Term Specialist Training Appointments (FTSTA), these will mirror the first two years of specialist training and can 'count towards' your training. However, only two years of the time spent in these posts can be counted towards training, any longer may allow you to gain valuable experience, but it will not bring you closer to your CCT. Those in FTSTA posts who are eligible, may compete to gain a place on a Specialist Training Programme.

Run through training is still in its infancy and may still undergo further reform. In the old system it was widely accepted that most graduates did not have a firm idea of what they wanted to specialise in and would spend several years as an SHO in various specialties, before making an *informed* choice. This method of finding one's vocation is likely to become a thing of the past with run through training, which allows far less flexibility. Some graduates entering medical school think they know what they want to do and will be pleased to press on with their training, but for the majority, committing to a specialty with only one year of post graduate experience is a daunting prospect. Some will be unable to secure a F1/F2 post in the specialty to which they will apply and so will have no real experience of it. Also, the system as it stands makes no realistic provision for doctors who wish to change specialty once they have embarked on a training programme. One imagines they will be able to reapply and 'start again', but this issue has not really been addressed by MMC/PMETB.

However, things like 'taster weeks' in other specialties can be incorporated into the F2 year. The introduction by some specialities of a second competitive entry point before ST3 may help those in the wrong careers to 'escape', but it remains to be seen how easy it will be for them to return to the beginning and gain entry onto another speciality's scheme.

However the system evolves, it is imperative that whilst at medical school you really take the opportunity to embrace each specialty as you pass through it, and to be proactive in securing 'tasters', because the next time you come into contact with what you think is your chosen specialty, it may be the last one you ever do…

Postgraduate examinations

For each specialty there is a governing College who is responsible for setting the postgraduate curriculum and examinations and maintaining the standards of training. The role of these Colleges is changing as Postgraduate Medical Education and Training Board (PMETB) tries to take control of post graduate training. We await the outcome of this power struggle.

Before the words competency based training had been invented, the main stepping stones to your speciality training path were a series of examinations set by the appropriate college. These exams remain formidable hurdles, even to the seasoned examinee. Passing them earns you the right to become a 'Member' or 'Fellow' of your chosen college. At present, these exams must still be passed to allow career progression.

Governing college are currently as follows:
Royal College of Anaesthetists
Faculty of Pain Medicine of the Royal College of Anaesthetists
Royal College of Emergency Medicine
Royal College of General Practitioners
Royal College of Obstetricians & Gynaecologists
Royal College of Ophthalmologists
Royal College of Pathologists
- blood transfusion
- chemical pathology
- clinical immunology
- forensic pathology
- haematology
- histopathology
- immunopathology
- medical microbiology
Royal College of Physicians of the UK
Royal College of Physicians of Edinburgh
- cardiology
- clinical immunology
- clinical pharmacology
- communicable (infectious diseases)
- dermatology

- endocrinology and diabetes

- general (internal) medicine

- genito-urinary medicine (venereology)

- geriatrics

- haematology (see also pathology)

- neurology

- oncology (see also radiotherapy)

- paediatrics

- renal disease (nephrology)

- respiratory disease

- rheumatology

- tropical medicine

Royal College of Psychiatrists

- child psychiatry

- forensic psychiatry

- mental disability

- psychogeriatrics

- psychotherapy

Royal College of Radiologists

Royal College of Surgeons of England

Royal College of Surgeons of Edinburgh

- general surgery

- neurosurgery

- orthopaedics

- otorhinolaryngology

- paediatric surgery

- plastic surgery

- urology

Royal College of Physicians and Surgeons of Glasgow

Academic medicine

The number of doctors employed in academic medicine has been in decline in recent years. To address this, the governing bodies have allocated funding to attract trainees and a clinical fellowship post of up to three years can be taken with the potential for integration into the framework described above. A career in academic medicine can be furthered by taking a clinical lectureship position. F1 and F2 academic posts are also available and are open to graduates with a proven record of academic achievement and interest in research, publication and teaching. They incorporate research and clinical practice into the four month placements.

Other Medical Careers

Hospital doctoring versus general practice is not the only fork in the road for you as you progress; there are other options available to you: public health, forensic medicine, secure environment (prison) medicine and military medicine, as examples.

The tri-services will be present at university career days; they offer financial support during your medical school education in return for a commitment to serve the force in a medical capacity for six years following graduation. Your commission can be extended beyond that subject to mutual agreement. There are significant financial benefits as both student and junior doctor. There are also career advantages due to the nature of employment; most hospitals are delighted to have a doctor working for them for 'free'. This opens doors into specialist jobs which are very competitive to civilians. Also experience of Medicine in the Field is an experience unique to the military personnel. In addition, the Forces are very supportive of sporting excellence, giving their trainees time off for these commitments and for 'Adventurous Training Leave'.

Of course, Military doctors must take up regular postings, often to war zones, to provide a service both to the UK troops and to local civilians.

Useful links

The British Medical Association (BMA). www.bma.org.uk

RemedyUK (Pressure group set up by junior doctors to voice concerns about training reforms) www.remedyuk.org

The careers service of the British Medical Journal www.bmjcareers.com

The NHS homepage for Modernising Medical Careers www.mmc.nhs.uk

The Conference of Postgraduate Medical Deans (COPMeD). www.copmed.org.uk

The Postgraduate Medical Education and Training Board www.pmetb.org.uk

The General Medical Council www.gmc-uk.org

Medical careers in the armed services:
      www.royal-navy.mod.uk
      www.army.mod.uk
      www.rafcareers.com

The Financial Implications of Studying Graduate Medicine

Please note that the information included in this chapter is liable to change. The prices quoted in this chapter are correct for the 2009-10 academic year unless otherwise stated.

Having done a degree before, the thought of paying for another degree can seem daunting. This chapter aims to help you understand the expenses involved, and show you that there are a number of sources of income available to any prospective student.

Money Out

There are a surprising number of hidden costs that are involved in studying medicine. There are things that you may not have considered, like stethoscopes, the cost of undertaking an elective, and travelling to and from clinical placements.

Application and preparation costs

The largest financial demands when applying are application fees for entrance exams, if applicable. There is also the UCAS application fee, travel costs incurred on attending Open Days, and, if all goes well, interviews. At present, the UCAS application fee is £7 if you are applying to only one university for one course, or £17 if you are applying to more than one university. Many universities will also charge an additional fee on top of this if you are an overseas student. Most medical courses that you can apply for have an entrance exam. The details of these are found in chapter 8, but at the time of writing,

- BMAT costs £32.10 for UK applicants and £55.90 for other candidates if you apply before midnight on the 30th September 2009. Between 1st and 15th October, the charges are £64.20 and £111.80 respectively. There may also be an additional administration fee if you sit the test in an 'Open' centre. It may be possible to get test fees reimbursed later.

- GAMSAT costs £192 if you register up to 5pm on the 14th August 2009. It will cost another £50 if you register between then and 5pm on 28th August. Note that official practice questions & practice test add £55 to this total.

- UKCAT costs £60 for candidates taking the test in the EU before 31st August 2009 and £95 for other candidates. Between 1st September and 9th October 2009, the cost is £75 for candidates taking the UKCAT in the EU. There is a bursary available for UKCAT, but you must apply for this before sitting the test.

In preparing for entrance exams and interviews you may wish to buy appropriate reading material, as detailed in chapters 8 and 9, or alternatively attend one of the many exam or interview practice courses to give you an edge over other candidates.

Tuition fees

The 2006 academic year saw the introduction of increased tuition fees for courses that commence that year and thereafter. The fees are determined by the individual universities, but in 2009, most universities charged home students the maximum £3,225. The maximum fee should not rise by more than the rate of inflation before 2010. The amount you have to pay is determined by your status as Home, EU or International student. Your status as a Home or International classification is decided by the universities to which you apply; it is essential that you check with the individual university to ascertain your status.

On the whole, most universities define a Home student as one who is domiciled in the UK. You would need to show that you have the right of abode or indefinite leave to enter or remain in the UK, or a passport stamp which gives you the right of readmission to the UK. You need to have been 'ordinarily resident' in the UK throughout the 3 years immediately before the start of your course and the reason for your residence during that period should not have been wholly for the purpose of receiving full-time education. At most universities, an EU national who has been resident in the European Economic Area (EEA) throughout the 3 year period, for reasons other than full-time education, would also be classed as a Home student.

Most other students who do not fall within the Home Student or EU classification would be considered as International Students and be liable to pay considerably higher fees. Many graduate entry medicine courses exclude International Student applicants (see chapter 3). An international student could be asked to pay tuition fees anywhere between £10,000 - £25,000 per year, incrementally increasing with each ensuing year of the course. If you are an international student, it is advisable to contact your prospective medical school and check that you will be considered.

If you are an EU student you should contact EU_Team@slc.co.uk, or follow the links on: http://www.direct.gov.uk/studentfinance-eu

Tuition fee payment

Unlike those studying for a first degree, the government has decided that graduates who study for a second degree are liable to pay their tuition fees at the start of each academic year, and are not eligible for a tuition fee loan. With the fees themselves at £3,225, this is a large payment up front that must be considered. The government has tried to justify this by stating that the DfES is only seeking to help students who have not had the opportunity to experience Higher Education before. However, for the specifically designed graduate entry courses, this financial burden will be incurred in the first year only (see 'Money In', later), and even then many medical schools will let students spread this over the duration of the course.

This policy has caused some controversy for a number of reasons. Firstly, this will put off a number of potential students who may already have incurred a great deal of debt through their studies and limit the potential intake to those who can most afford it. Secondly, the policy itself is not in line with other healthcare degrees such as nursing and social work, where tuition fees are paid for students who already possess a degree. Despite many protestations against this, the government have refused to budge on this issue at the time of writing.

Living costs

Accommodation costs are detailed in the relevant University sections of chapter 3. The British Medical Association completed a survey in 2006/07 of medical student expenditure and found some enlightening facts that might assist in your own planning:

- The average monthly accommodation cost outside London was £308, while inside London it was £442.

- The average medical student's day-to-day living expenditure was £432-710 per month (outside London average £587- London average £674).

Living in halls will be on average cheaper than renting privately. Should you be living privately, don't forget to shop around for cheaper deals on utilities, insurance etc. on websites like www.uswitch.com or www.moneysupermarket.com.

Oxford & Cambridge Colleges may charge you extra in the form of a college fee, but there is a loan that you can take to specifically pay for this cost (see below).

Studying costs

In year one you will mostly incur set-up costs:
- Stethoscope (ranging in price from £30-150)
- Small library of books (ranging from the low hundreds up to a thousand pounds). Of course, eBay can reduce the cost.
- Stationery supplies
- Home computer (some medical schools recommend certain specifications)
- At least one decent set of smart clothes

When you reach the penultimate and final years of your course:
- Travel and on-site hospital accommodation for clinical placements (before possible reimbursement by your University or NHS Grant (see later in the chapter)).
- Revision books and courses from e.g. The Medical Defence Union (MDU) and the Medical Protection Society (MPS). With

a membership discount they can cost around £60-225 per course.

- Several more smart sets of clothes

Elective costs

One of the brightest blips on your radar as a medical student is the elective period. This is your chance to travel to fascinating far-flung places and experience life and medicine in a different context. Although some students choose to stay in the UK for their elective, the majority travel abroad, and some have more than one elective. In general the elective period lasts between 3-12 weeks, but some courses offer no elective period (see chapter 3). The BMA survey in 2006/07 put the average cost of a first elective at £2,023.

During your elective period, costs include travel, accommodation, living expenses, plus extra things such as health insurance, HIV prophylaxis of about £100 and visas. Funds mostly come from students' own pockets, but you may be able to obtain financial assistance from your university, some of the Medical Societies or governmental help. www.medicsworld.co.uk offers elective advice including a list of the various organizations offering financial awards for elective travel.

Travel costs

The BMA survey or 2006/07 showed that half of respondents ran a car, with average standing costs (i.e. excluding petrol) of £867. The average amount spent on travel to clinical placements with peripheral attachment was £253. The Department of Health provides funding to your medical school to assist in funding clinical placements. This includes a small portion of money for your travel and on-site accommodation costs. For details of the rates, see the NHS Student Bursaries website on www.nhsbsa.nhs.uk/students, and see later in the chapter.

Society memberships

Should you feel the need to network and broaden your horizons, medical societies such as the British Medical Association (BMA) can offer excellent sources of information and contact with the medical world which you will soon be entering. The BMA is free for the first year of your medical course, £30 for the second year, and £36 p.a. thereafter. Other societies include the Royal Society of Medicine (RSM) – which costs £40 p.a. for an online subscription and, if you are female, the Medical Women's Federation (MWF) – which costs £15 p.a.

The BMA News will keep you abreast of how the medical profession operates and changes and reading the letters page can give you an idea of the prevailing opinions of working doctors and students. Also, these societies offer money prizes to medical students with obvious financial and CV advantages to the winners.

Money In

If the above has you really worried, don't despair! Help is out there, and there are many options available to you, especially if you are persistent and creative.

Government Help

There are two departments which the future graduate medical student can apply to for funding: The Department of Health (DoH) & The Department for Education and Skills (DfES), both of which are looked at in turn below. The information below is accurate at time of writing, but it would be advisable to contact your local authority and ask them to send you a form and instructions regarding what funding you are eligible for – especially regarding funding from the DfES. The local authority that will provide you with funds relates to your address when the application is sent, not that of your prospective university. The DfES recommend that prospective students begin their application for these loans when the application process is underway, rather than waiting until a place is offered, but in practice this is unusual. The DfES provides a booklet called "A Guide to Financial Support for Higher Education Students 2009/10", which provides information for prospective students, and may be helpful to understand the vagaries of the application process.

DoH/NHS Bursary for tuition fees

Graduate medical students are eligible for an NHS bursary to cover tuition fees. If you are taking the 4 year accelerated course, the bursary is available for years 2 to 4. If on a longer 5 or 6 year course, the bursary is only available for the 5th (and if applicable the 6th) year. These will pay for your tuition fees in full, softening the blow a little. Being a bursary, no repayments are due.

Eligibility criteria are detailed in the NHS student bursary document and on their website, but it is for home students or students who have been resident in England for 3 years prior to commencement of the course. EU students will receive an 'EU fees only' award, which will cover the cost of tuition fees only.

DoH/NHS Bursary

There is also a means-tested maintenance bursary available from the DoH, but this is only available for the same period as the DoH help for tuition fees, i.e. years 2 to 4 for the accelerated course, or year 5 (& 6) on a standard course. Although the DoH publishes a guide to the amount you can expect, it is complicated. In 2008/09 the means-tested maintenance amount, i.e. the basic bursary, for London students per annum was £3,306, for non-London students is £2,739, and living at their parent's home was £2,287 p.a. This amount is increased with the following extra additions to the basic bursary, for 2008/09:

- An additional amount per week of course above 30 weeks + 3 days duration; £103p.w. for London students, £80p.w. for non-London students & £53p.w. for those living at their parent's home. If your course is longer than 45 weeks in duration in the year, then you will receive 52 weeks worth of funding (i.e. 22 weeks of £103 plus the basic amount).
- Dependent's Allowance: £2,573p.a. for a dependent spouse or first child and £525p.a. for subsequent children
- Childcare Allowance: pays childcare for up to £123.25p.w. for one child, and up to £182.25p.w. for 2 or more children. Note that all the every childcare allowance is calculated individually based on your exact circumstances, and that the childcare has to be from registered or approved providers.
- Disabled Student's Allowance: up to £20,000p.a. for a helper, £5,031p.a. for equipment, and £1,680p.a. for 'other costs' such as travel that has been actually, reasonably and necessarily incurred.
- Practice Placement Expenses: Reimbursements for car (including parking, tolls etc.), motorbike & public transport usage to travel to clinical placements - provided costs are in excess of your normal daily travel costs from your term-time residence to your college. You can also claim back excess accommodation costs. This is means tested.

- Hardship Support Funds: available if in severe financial difficulty.
- Parents Learning Allowance: pays up to £1,270p.a. to students with dependent child/children, subject to income assessment.
- Maternity/Paternity/Adoption Leave: new mothers will continue to receive NHS bursary for up to 45 weeks, depending on individual circumstances. New fathers will continue to receive their bursary for up to 4 weeks whilst taking an authorised period of paternity leave.

Please check http://www.nhsbsa.nhs.uk/students for updates, and the explanatory booklet 'Financial Help for Healthcare Students Academic Year 2008/09 – Booklet 2'. At time of writing, an updated version of this for 2009/10 was not available, but it is reasonable to expect this version to be available in time for the next academic year.

The DoH Bursary is means-tested. For students aged under 25 at the start of the academic year, the parental income is assessed, whereas for independent students, parental income is not assessed but a spouse's contribution may be. Spouse here includes your partner through marriage/civil partnership, and although the document says that you need to include "your opposite sex partner if you live together as though you were married", enforcing this could be difficult.

The DoH/NHS bursaries restrict the amount of the DfES maintenance loan (see below) that will be made available to you while in receipt of the bursary – according to some sources this may reduce the amount of loan available by approximately 50%. If you are an EU national you may not normally qualify for a bursary. You may also not be eligible to receive the

DoH/NHS bursary if you take an intercalated BSc year during your graduate entry programme – check with your medical school for details.

NHS Hardship Grant

If you are a medical student who has exhausted all other sources of financial help, you may, exceptionally, be eligible for a NHS Hardship Grant. You may apply if you are eligible for the NHS Bursary, have taken all available entitlements, in which case you need to write to The Section Manager at NHS Student Bursaries (see www.nhsstudentgrants.co.uk). You will need to send evidence that you have already applied for a student loan and university access to learning funds.

DfES Tuition Fee Loan

If you have attended a publicly funded degree in the UK before, you are not expected to be eligible for tuition fee loans, even if you did not receive a tuition fee loan for your first degree. If your degree came from either a private university, or you studied overseas, then it is recommended that you contact your local authority for further guidance (even private university degrees are subsidised to some extent). If you are an EU student that previously studied abroad, then you are eligible for a non-income assessed loan.

DfES Maintenance /Special Support /Higher Education Grant

As for tuition fee loans, if you have attended a publicly funded degree in the UK before, you are not eligible for a maintenance grant, a special support grant, or a higher education grant.

DfES Maintenance Loan

The maintenance loan is available for students who have been on a publicly funded degree in the UK before and for their next degree are studying for a professional qualification, which includes medicine. The amount that is available varies, since it is means-tested, has a London weighting, and is reduced if you accept the DoH bursary mentioned before, which will reduce the amount of loan available by approximately 50%. The loan is administered by the Student Loans Company (SLC). It accrues in line with the Retail Price Index, i.e. 4.8% in 2007/08, and will be repayable on graduation when you begin to earn £15,000 or more. For students starting their course in September 2008 or later, the Government will write off student loan balances (except for arrears) which are left unpaid 25 years after their liability to repay commenced, which is the April after the course has finished.

Below are the rates available for 2009/10:

Maximum Full Year loan rate

- *Student living at home £3,838*
- *Student living away from home, in London £6,928*
- *Student living away from home, outside London £4,950*

Maximum Final Year loan rate

- *Student living at home £3,483*
- *Student living away from home, in London £6,307*
- *Student living away from home, outside London £4,583*

*note that this is the maximum loan, and can be reduced through means testing and if you successfully apply for an NHS bursary, this amount will be reduced by approximately 50%.

As with the DoH/NHS bursary, this allowance is means-tested. As before, the household income will be measured against your status as 'dependent' or 'independent'. Dependent students are those whose parents' income is taken into account. Independent students are aged over 25; or have been married before the start of the academic year for which they are applying for support; or have supported themselves for at least 3 years; or have no living parents; or have care of a child or young person under 18. However, you need to be a home student to qualify. Note if you have a spouse/civil partner then their income will be taken into account for means testing.

DfES Additional sources of help

Additional sources of help from the DfES/your LA include:

- Parent's Learning Allowance- up to £1,508 p.a. This is a non-repayable allowance for course-related costs for a full time student with dependent children. This depends on your income and that of your dependents. It is for course related costs like books, material and travel.
- Child Tax Credit from HM Revenue and Customs (HMRC) – students with dependent children are eligible for Child Tax Credit. The website www.hmrc.gov.uk/taxcredits will allow you to calculate how much you can gain, and allows you to make an on-line claim.
- Adult Dependent's Grant- a non-repayable grant up to £2,643 p.a. for full-time students with adult dependents. How much you get is based on your income and that of your adult dependents.
- Childcare Grant- this is a non-repayable grant of up to £148.75 p.w. for one child (85% of actual costs of up to £175 a week), or

up to £255 p.w. for 2 or more children (85% of actual costs of up to £300 a week).

- Disabled Students Allowance (DSAs) – a non-repayable allowance for students with disabilities which is designed to help with the extra costs there are as a result of undertaking the course and as a direct result of the disability/specific learning difficulty. This does not depend on your income or that of your family. The allowance can be up to £5,161 for specialist equipment for the whole course, up to £20,520p.a. for a non-medical helper allowance, a general disabled student's allowance of up to £1,724p.a., and any extra travel costs incurred. Post-graduates are also eligible for this.   There is also a DSA for postgraduate study – a non-repayable allowance of up to £10,260p.a. for a course that has an entry requirement of at least a first degree and lasts for at least one academic year. However, if you have received a bursary from the NHS or the General Social Care Council, an award from a Research Council, or university award which includes support for disabilities, you are **not** eligible for these allowances, although there are equivalent allowances through the NHS bursary scheme..

- College Fee Loan for specific second degrees at Oxford & Cambridge – students with a UK honours degree from a publicly funded institution, and who are studying a second undergraduate degree at either Oxford or Cambridge may apply for a College Fee Loan to help with the extra college fee which the Oxford or Cambridge college may charge.

However, being in receipt of the DoH/NHS bursary may affect eligibility for a number of these allowances.

DfES Further Information

The following website provides more information should you require it: http://www.direct.gov.uk/studentfinance

For advice on paying your loan, the financial help available, the application process, timetable and their progress in assessing your application, then you can call the Student Loans Company on 0845 300 50 90, or look at http://www.direct.gov.uk/studentfinance

Alternatively, contact your local authority and speak to their Higher Education Funding Department or its equivalent for advice.

Other sources of income

Hardship and Access to Learning Funds
The DfES has made these funds available with priority to particular students such as those with children, students with disability, mature students and those in their final year. These funds are designed for extra help if you are in hardship and need extra financial support.

Access to Learning Funds are paid in addition to a full student loan after recommendation from the University. Usually, the maximum amount available is £500 per year. Applications for Hardship Funds can usually only be made once any other Student Loans Company (SLC) funding has been received. The eligibility requirements are the same as for the SLC loan but you need to demonstrate to your university that you are in real financial difficulty and need help. These funds can be given as a grant or loan, and it is at the university's discretion whether to award this as a lump sum or in instalments. They are often restricted to Home/EU students. It is usually awarded after you begin a course, but if you think you will need help before you start, then it is recommended that you contact your university.

Government Benefits for Students

Some students may be eligible to apply for benefits such as Housing Benefit and Council Tax Benefit. If you think this may be you, then go to: http://www.dwp.gov.uk/advisers/rr2/students/

Scholarships

Individual universities have their own scholarships, such as scholarships for excellence in sport and music. They will also have scholarships unique to that institution. One to look out for is the alumni scholarship, especially if the University at which you are studying graduate entry medicine is where you previously studied. Many of these scholarships can remain untouched and are worth investigation.

Potential funding for elective

The Royal Colleges and other professional associations offer monetary awards to medical students who may have an interest in taking an elective. These awards have specific conditions, and you can get an amount from between £50 - £2,000. All of these colleges and countless other sources of funding for a medical elective are listed on the BMA's 'Directory of sources for funding an elective':

Charitable Foundations

Charities are a largely untapped source of income for many students. This is because the amount of money that is given out is usually relatively small when compared to the amounts that can be gained from government funding, and many students are not inclined to trawl through the internet and relevant books. As such, much of this potential funding goes unused. Do note that most funds and charities have a limited remit; very few are prepared to sponsor a student throughout the duration of the degree, and cannot provide immediate financial assistance.

There are numerous trusts that give out awards according to the profession of your parents or spouse, or your geographical location, or where you were brought up, or where you went to school, and grants for those with specific degrees or nationalities. It is recommended that you look at The Directory of Grant Making Trusts, The Educational Grants Directory, or A Guide to Grants For Individuals In Need – all published by the Directory Of Social Change (DSC) – http://www.dsc.org.uk, and available either in libraries or the DSC charitable library (& bookshop) based in Euston, London. There is also a search engine for scholarships available on http://www.scholarship-search.org.uk.

However, the best list of charities and trusts can be found via The Education Grants Advisory Services (EGAS) of the Family Welfare Association which gives information and advice on potential sources of educational funding. The EGAS was established in 1962 to offer students, especially disadvantaged students, expert guidance and advice to enable them to secure funding for education and training. Their website has an excellent search engine, which finds relevant Trusts for you to contact based on your own personal information and circumstances. They can be found on:

http://www.family-action.org.uk/section.aspx?id=1037
Educational Grants Advisory Service (EGAS)
501-505 Kingsland Road
London E8 4AU
0207 254 6251.

A number of grants are specific to the study of medicine, and/or a second degree. Information can be found in the DSC books, the website listed above, or a list of alternative sources of funding for graduate medicine which is available from BMA Charities (0207 383 6142/6334). These sources are liable to be updated annually, and that extra information will give you a slight edge over your peers to receive this funding.

The procedure for applying to trusts differs widely although most trusts require either a letter or application form and some form of reference. If there is no clear guidance given by the trust, you should write to the trust detailing the type of funding required, your personal circumstances and academic background, including relevant supporting evidence.

Before applying to a trust, always check the often extraordinary eligibility criteria. Do not waste your own and the trust's time by submitting an application for which you are not truly eligible. Keep in mind that you usually need a confirmed place at University before your application will be considered. Do not apply to every charity in the same year because the charities know each other and tend only to offer money to those not in receipt of moneys from any other source.

If you are fortunate to receive an award from the trusts, write and thank them, and list it on your CV.

Other good sources of information are:
- Funderfinder: http://www.funderfinder.org.uk/ - a website that gives advice and information on grants.
- Money4MedStudents: http://www.money4medstudents.org – a comprehensive website that gives good, impartial advice for present and future medical students.

Commercial bank loans

Most high street banks offer professional studies loans, usually from the second year of the course onwards, but only 17% of medical students have a commercial bank loan on graduating. Those that do, have an average graduating loan of £9,568. With a professional studies loan, repayments would commonly commence 6 months – 1 year after graduation, with interest charged somewhere near but above the bank's base rate. These banks also tend to have loans specifically for elective costs. A student bank account confers larger than usual overdraft options. 55% of medical students have an overdraft on graduating which averages £1,426.

A career development loan is also a deferred repayment high street bank loan, but while you are studying the DfES pays the interest. For further information go to www.lifelonglearning.co.uk/cdl/. You can borrow between £300 and £8,000 to help you fund up to 2 years of learning.

Work part-time

Working part-time whilst studying for an intensive graduate entry medical degree is achievable with considerable time management skills. It can be particularly beneficial if you find part-time work in medicine, or allied to it, e.g. as a Medical Secretary/Administrator or as an Auxiliary Nurse. This can improve your breadth of medical knowledge and keep you up to speed on the ward environment. The BMA 2006/07 survey found that 24% of medical students have a job in term-time (and on average earn £1,840), and 51% work in the summer holidays (and on average earn £1,248). Finally, if you work during your holidays and expect to earn under £5,435 (known as your personal allowance) in the tax year, ask your employer for a P38 (S) form. With this, your employer will be able to pay you without deducting tax. Even if they do deduct tax, you may be eligible for a rebate (see below).

Tax Rebates

Your current or previous employer may have taxed you at a rate that assumed you would be working for the entire tax year. At the start your course, you would have the right to reclaim it from the Inland Revenue. To do this, you will need to send in the originals of both your P60 & P45 form(s), payslips and any information that you have about your employment & benefit history, along with a covering letter describing that you have paid too much tax, with your name, address and NI number to the relevant tax office (keeping a photocopy of the originals). This can take many months to appear with a response (meaning that you will likely be receiving the money around halfway through your second year). However, it is easily possible that you will be paid back large amounts, and so is well worth the wait. If you have any queries, then call your local Tax Office.

Student discounts

Your National Union of Students (NUS) card will gain you discounts of about 10% on products from many companies. You can find more information at the NUS website: www.nusonline.co.uk. As a full-time student you can also get student discounts on rail travel (using a Young Person's Railcard) and other transport services (e.g. the National Express Coachcard). Also, if you live in London, you may be eligible for a student Oyster Card (for discounted travelling on public transport), and there may be similar schemes in other towns and cities. You will also have access to student discounted travel through the STA travel company. There are numerous hidden student discounts that are easily unearthed with a little bit of effort. For example, if you live in a house with only students you will be exempt from paying council tax, and being a student may entitle you to cheaper or even free dental, optician, & pharmacy costs – you can pick up a HC1 form from your local hospital, calling 0845 850 1116, or going onto http://www.ppa.org.uk/index.htm (the PPA will assess your circumstances at the time of application, so should you work in the holidays, it is recommended that you apply during term-time).

Overall

Although the thought of medicine, and how to pay for it, can be overwhelming, it is important to remember that it is the passion inside you for the profession itself that is driving you forward, and many will take the financial 'pain' involved over the short-term to do such a fantastic career in the long-term. Unfortunately, medicine is not as stable and secure a career as it used to be, but many doors are open to you as a doctor. And, as this chapter has (hopefully) shown you, there are many different options and sources of help available to guide through your course and onto the other side.

Summary

- Costs will include fees, travel, accommodation, study costs, and electives. The application procedure itself can run into the hundreds
- If in any doubt, check your status with regards to Home, EU or international status. Different universities define this in different ways
- Some universities will ask about your financial planning at interview

For Home students:
- Income could include a DoH bursary for tuition fees for years 2-4 of a specific graduate entry programme, DoH bursary for living costs, DfES maintenance loan, and private loans

Work Experience

Work experience defines a good candidate. For many medical students it represents a seminal period in a journey of self-discovery that led them to training to become a doctor; a transition from idealism to reality. There is no substitute for tangible experience in a healthcare setting where potential candidates can examine what it means to be a health professional. Medical schools give much weight to work experience as a tool in itself at interview. Just doing work experience is little in itself – anyone can say that they spent a year as a care assistant at their local hospital, but with nothing learnt there is nothing gained. At interview you will impress not for what you did, but rather what it did to you.

Quality and quantity are important - it can be of the highest standard, but if you only gained two weekends of experience in the past year, your commitment to truly dedicating yourself to medicine will be in question. Work experience is not a token gesture, or a box to be ticked. It is vital to your hopes and aspirations. To be able to present yourself as a potential doctor, you have to have some awareness of what it is to actually *be* a doctor. This is borne out of work experience that has been reflected on, and resonates with you in your application.

Why Work Experience?

As mentioned in chapter 2, the reason for obtaining relevant work experience is not simply to satisfy the medical schools' requirements, but to be as certain as you possibly can be that medicine is the right choice for you. Embarking on a medical career, especially as a mature individual, is an enormous commitment, and you would not be the first graduate entry student to feel that they have used up their life's quota of mistakes and wanderings. Most candidates reading this book cannot afford, either emotionally or financially, to make a poor decision about something so hugely important. Without work experience you cannot make an informed decision, you are unlikely to be able to write a convincing personal statement, or compete at interview. Yet it is curious how many candidates are convinced of their desire to be a doctor, when their knowledge of the subject barely extends beyond their personal experiences of having their appendix removed and of nursing their grandfather for a few days after his hip replacement.

Conversely, do not think that you are necessarily in a better position simply because you are able to produce a long list of different experiences with different eminent Consultants. Whilst variety is great, the benefit of work experience comes from a far more humble insight than a seemingly showy list of contacts.

What constitutes quality work experience?

Quality does not relate to the seniority or prestige of your responsible superior or mentor, nor the setting, but to what you actually did and what you learnt from it. The gold standard is full-time work as a care assistant in a hospital or nursing home, and whilst many medical students relate how they gave up their 'successful career' to throw themselves fully into pursuing a career in medicine, this is not possible for everyone. However, it is vital that you get the chance to spend time with sick people who may be frustrated or confused, vulnerable and in need of help; exactly what you will have to deal with as a junior doctor. This time has to be a commitment and something you have invested yourself in.

In addition, it is sterling to have witnessed a good doctor in action. Do you have some of the same skills as that doctor? Can you relate to the way they conduct themselves? What do these doctors do well? Have you seen a poor doctor? What made him sub-optimal? You will have thoughts on these issues already, but they will become far more profound when framed in the context of hands-on work experience.

Quality work experience, whatever it may be, is reflected in the effect it has had on you. If it developed your awareness of the responsibilities, challenges, trials and tribulations of what of means to be a clinician, you're clearly going to benefit greatly.

What experiences should I be seeking?

This is the question most candidates ask, but it is the wrong one. The question you should be asking yourself is 'what should I be learning from my experiences? How did it enhance and expand my knowledge and understanding?' The 'gold standard' experience is perhaps impossible due to your circumstances, or might not even be available. There are a limited amount of vacancies as health care professionals or other paramedical work. Find what you can and commit yourself to it – there is a certain amount of kudos in having done everything you could to seek out tangible opportunities. What is not acceptable is "I couldn't find anything"; there is always something out there, but it may take time to find it. Which candidate's resolve would you admire more:

- "I tried to get work as a health care assistant but my PCT was in debt and not taking on staff so there didn't seem to be anything available"
- "I tried to get work as a health care assistant but my PCT was in debt and not taking on staff, so I sent my CV to local care agencies, and while I waited for something to come up I volunteered at the District General"

How do I make it tangible? - getting the most out of your work experience

Satisfactory demonstration of attributes such as empathy, intellectual ability, ability to accept responsibility and handle stress, communication, teamwork and so on is not dependent on the type of experience, but on your analysis, criticism and insight into that experience.

During your chosen experiences, you should try to seize the opportunity to gain an understanding in as many aspects of healthcare as you can. This may include:

- Being able to recognise and empathise with the needs of patients
- Communicate with patients and the medical staff, where appropriate
- Recognise what makes a good doctor
- Recognise the skills that *you* have that reflect those of a good doctor
- Make the most of any opportunities to develop those skills
- Recognise the importance of the multi-disciplinary team
- Consider the problems facing patients, relatives, doctors and other healthcare professionals
- Consider your own prejudices, fears and concerns

This is by no means an exhaustive list of issues that you might dwell on during your work experience. Indeed, a list somewhat detracts from the preferred notion that you gain an understanding that is an intricately woven ensemble of practicalities, emotions, finances, ethics and management issues.

If you refer to chapter 2 you will start to gain insight into what makes a good doctor, and the reality of studying medicine. Chapter 7 and 9 highlight what the medical schools are looking for and how you might demonstrate those qualities. If you read *Tomorrow's Doctors* alongside the medical school prospectuses, you will gain an even more detailed view of what makes a good doctor.

For all of the skills mentioned throughout this book and elsewhere, try to witness and achieve them during your work experience. Empathise with patients. Talk to them, listen to their needs. Ask them about their care. Be kind. Be thoughtful. Be responsible. Talk to other healthcare professionals. Empathise with them too. What are the problems facing doctors, other healthcare professionals, patients and their relatives? How do you feel about financial constraints? How do you feel about the patient who is largely 'responsible' for their own illness? Do you think they are owed a lesser standard of care or are they an equal individual? How do you feel about sickness, suffering and death? How do you feel about bodily fluids, unsightly conditions and nasty smells?

Keeping a diary – assisting reflection and evaluation

You may find it very useful to keep a diary of your experiences. Whilst it might help you to note meetings and departments attended and so forth, the key use of your retrospective diary should be to note memorable moments and interesting patients, your own emotions, and things you have witnessed. When you write your personal statement, or prepare for interview, this collection of ideas and emotions will be of enormous help to you in relating your thoughts in a fresh and dynamic way.

For each of the examples and situations that you note in your diary, also try to empathise and rationalise the situation. Why did a patient behave aggressively? Was the doctor unkind? Were the patient and/or doctor frightened? Was the patient confused? Were they lonely? Were they on medication that might alter their mood? You may find that by communicating and empathising with that patient, you may not only answer these questions, you might also provide a great deal of support to a patient in need when other healthcare professionals simply cannot afford the time. Also try to think realistically about how you would feel if you were caring for such a patient in addition to many others. Take advantage of opportunities, for instance; if you witness a practical procedure, take the time to go back and talk to the patient about how it was for them.

Similarly, when you see a good doctor in action, think about every facet of why that doctor was good. What was their body language like? What questions did they ask? Did they listen and really pick up on the patient's underlying message? What information did they give? How did they give it? Why not ask patients what they think makes a good doctor? And most importantly, ask yourself if you have these qualities. Can you demonstrate them? Can you improve on them?

Be careful not to be a maverick and focus on the flaws of the system (for you will see many). Of course it can be easier and sometimes more natural to exemplify skills by considering the consequences of their absence. It is important to recognise inadequacies; they exist and one needs to be realistic. However, remember that, on balance, you should *want* to work within the NHS with patients and health care professionals, rather than feel that it is something you could simply *cope* with.

Useful sources of work experience

There are many opportunities through which you will be able to gain real insight into some of the issues listed above.

Care Work

- Care work/ care assistant at residential home/ care home for the elderly/disabled (e.g. residential care home for children with autism)
- Volunteer at hospital/ volunteer auxiliary/ ward volunteer
- Volunteer at a soup kitchen, centre for the homeless
- Mentoring and tutoring
- Volunteer Counselling
- Befriending services to disadvantaged/ elderly
- Community work

These are simply some ideas to hopefully spark your own imagination, or nudge you in a useful direction. There is no suggestion that you do all of these things. For some more thoughtful people, just one type of high quality experience may be sufficient for them to gain the sort of insight that is encouraged. However, even this type of candidate is likely to need to spend a significant period of time in their role. Indeed, Bristol University have actually stated that candidates should consider at least 3 months' experience as a Healthcare Assistant or similar.

Shadowing

Although shadowing rarely affords any hands-on exposure, it is important that you shadow a doctor, especially a junior one, to give you valuable insight into their work. It cannot replace care work or similar, but provides a valuable adjunct opportunity. You could also learn a great deal from shadowing other healthcare professionals. For instance, if you gain shadowing experience at a General Practice, try to observe the

Community Nurses, in addition to the GP. Similarly, you may find that working with physiotherapists could be a rewarding opportunity, and so forth. Many candidates get very excited about the prospect of spending time with, say, a top Consultant Neurosurgeon. Of course, you would not turn down this opportunity, as it is a wonderful one, but bare in mind the limitations of what it tells you about an average patient's needs and an average doctor's workload. Also, those doctors who are now consultants were medical students when trends were different, and they may inadvertently encourage an 'unfashionable' outlook. You may find it more relevant to attempt to spend time with a more recently qualified doctor and to spend time 'on take' (i.e. responsible for all hospital admissions during that shift). You could always go for the trial by fire approach and spend a Friday night shift in A&E.

Other useful experiences and opportunities through work and hobbies.
You may be able to additionally demonstrate transferable skills through experiences not directly related to medicine, which can be particularly useful for the busy professional and/or parent/spouse. For instance, for those candidates who play sport, you may find that there are some very rewarding opportunities if you simply change the emphasis of your training; try performing an internet search on your own sport, with other keywords such as disability, children and volunteer, for instance.

Experiences for candidates already working in a healthcare setting
If you are currently a pharmacist, PhD student, NHS manager, social worker or any other professional involved with patients, healthcare or research, you will clearly have extensive insight into your particular field. However, your role could be narrow, and also biased. Particularly for those working in a relatively closeted research environment, gaining hands-on care experience is important. Aside from improving your

insight, you will be able to more easily demonstrate yourself to be a well-rounded, interested and motivated individual with demonstrable human qualities.

Reading

Although not strictly work experience, it is useful to include here the notion of reading widely. In much the same way as your medical knowledge develops at medical school, your understanding of current affairs and advancements in medicine will be superior if built over time. Read relevant newspaper articles, perhaps subscribe to a journal, and maintain objectivity by always considering the different impacts on all parties affected by any article that you read. Indeed, when reading a newspaper article on a recent development consider what it means to patients. Use your work experience to ask patients what the story means to them.

Personal Experiences

Although not work experience as such, your insight into medicine through your own personal experience as a relative or carer may be very useful. If these experiences form a large part of your desire to become a doctor, it may be worth taking the time to think about your unique situation from other people's point of view and to try, in so far as it's possible, to put the experience into more objective and general terms. Taking time to reflect and articulate on these experiences prior to interview can be very useful.

Work Experience Action Plan – So what do I do?

Care Experience
- Devote a considerable amount of time to it.
- Start planning and obtaining it as soon as possible.

There may be impediments to swiftly undertaking positions such as CRB checks and rigorous application procedures.

- Make enquiries

  Use the internet to search, use libraries and local directories to find out what is in your area. Get ideas from other people.

- Sign up with agencies

  Job centres and employment agencies serve the care industry

- Assess the suitability of a 'host'

  Make a list of what is out there – prioritise what is best for you and what you want to get out of it.

- Visit institutions

  Make yourself known – if there's nothing available make sure they have your details on file.

- Don't give up or be discouraged

  Keep making phone-calls etc (obviously without being a harassment)

Do highlight the fact that you are volunteering (if that is what you are doing). Most institutions do not have extensive funds and extra help can be gratefully received. However, there is significant administrative hassle for the institution just to accept a volunteer so you may find that you have to prove yourself more than you expected. Nevertheless, this is a good opportunity to practise demonstrating your interest and commitment to healthcare.

Shadowing

- Make your intentions known at your local hospital

  The front desk should direct you to the relevant department such as personnel or academic services. In person can be better than a phone-call.

- Allow time for any checks and plan ahead

To be anyone anywhere in a hospital these days you have to observe protocol and can't just wander around.

- Try and use any connections you may have

  Knowing a doctor even through a friend or acquaintance may be a way in. Your GP may have some suggestions, but for confidentiality reasons you may not be able to shadow at your surgery.

You essentially need a doctor to take responsibility for your being in the hospital. You will find some hospitals very helpful and others less so. Most hospitals have a good Patient Advice and Liaison Service (PALS). They offer patient advice and support, and deal with comments and complaints. They are often enthusiastic about your interest, will provide valuable information and help you to find other useful contacts.

If you are really stuck, you could also ask the hospital switchboard to bleep one of the junior doctors, for instance the Mess president. Understandably, many switchboards will not put you through without a specific name, and if you do get through, you do run the risk of interrupting a busy junior doctor. Better times of the day are lunchtime and late afternoon. Do not ask to be put through to anyone on call. If you manage to speak to one of the juniors this way, be polite and concise, and you should be received reasonably. If switch will not put you through to any of the doctors, you could ask to be put through to the people who organise the junior doctor teaching. They will have regular contact with the juniors and may be willing to ask some of them for you. Another approach, which is minimal hassle, but likely to be a poor return, would be to send the hospital a handful of letters and politely ask that they be circulated to the house officers. There are many other approaches of this nature, just be polite and don't take it personally if people are short with you.

Some hospitals are so inundated with requests for work experience that they provide specific programmes. These are often designed with school leavers in mind and are therefore often organised for the start of the summer. However, if you are too late, you might at least be able to speak to the organiser who will clearly have good insight into your needs.

Candidates (well, those nearing the application deadline without relevant experience) invariably moan about how difficult it is to get work experience. It can be obtained with time and perseverance, motivation and a positive outlook, and excusing yourself from the task will not be received positively. Once gained it will stand you in good stead; but only if it was meaningful and you took time for reflection.

Summary

- Work experience is necessary for you to make an informed decision, for your personal statement, and to compete at interview.
- Care work is the gold standard to see the humble side of medicine.
- Shadowing is necessary; a junior doctor will give you more insight than a senior doctor.
- Start looking early. There's plenty out there, but it takes time.
- You must learn from your work experience. Keep a reflective diary.
- Talk to patients, doctors and other staff. Read about relevant aspects of their care and illness in the national press, textbooks and journals.

The Personal Statement

Part of the process of applying to university or college involves the submission of a 'personal statement' to the Universities & Colleges Admissions Service (UCAS; their website is www.ucas.co.uk). Some universities require you to write an additional statement which is invariably quite similar to the personal statement. Most medical schools include consideration of your personal statement in their decision-making process. Even if your chosen schools will not read your personal statement, you should still think of the entire UCAS form as an opportunity to rationalise your desire to study medicine and as a chance to make a first impression. Writing a personal statement is seen by many as one of the most difficult parts of the UCAS form.

Graduate entry medical schools using the UCAS Personal Statement (or personal statements on other supplementary forms) as part of their shortlisting process.

Birmingham	Yes	Newcastle	Yes
Bristol	Yes	Nottingham	No
Cambridge	Yes	Oxford	Yes
Imperial	Yes	Queen Mary's	Yes
Keele	Yes	Southampton	Yes
Kings*	No	St George's	No
Leicester	Yes	Swansea	Yes
Liverpool	Yes	Warwick	Yes

*NB. Kings will read your personal statement for consideration for the standard entry course.

What sorts of things should go into your Personal Statement?

Some people fear that they will never have enough material, whilst others feel that the space is far too small to allow himself or herself justice. Of course, some candidates just see how it works out. Whichever group you belong to, you will need to spend a significant amount of time on the statement and you should expect to revise your text many times before settling on the final form and content.

There is a lot of guidance available in the school prospectuses and websites about what qualities the medical school are looking for. Chapter 2 discusses in some detail the essence of Tomorrow's Doctors. Although different schools might place a slightly different emphasis on different skills, they are all seeking essentially the same common endpoint. That is not to say that all schools are looking for one type of person, but they are looking for candidates who demonstrate suitable potential. The qualities and characteristics likely to be of interest to a medical school, especially of a graduate applicant, might include:

- Convincing explanation of the candidate's desire to study medicine
- Commitment to a career in medicine
- Intellectual and academic strength
- An empathic attitude
- Achievements (in addition to academic achievements)
- A realistic attitude about the profession and the course
- Self-motivation
- Evidence of an ability to apply oneself to a task

- Good organisational skills
- Growth as a person
- A 'well rounded' personality
- Demonstration of a wide range of interests
- Awareness of current developments

These types of skills are all potential elements of a good personal statement; you should be able to make additions to this list after studying the medical school prospectuses and the first section of this book. A strong candidate will be able to demonstrate, largely from their work experience, why they would make a good doctor. Chapter 6 discusses how you might obtain good work experience.

Getting Started

Before actually beginning to draft your personal statement, or indeed before reading much more of this chapter, you may find it useful to carry a notebook with you and to start making a list of things about yourself that might form elements of your personal statement. Keep your list easily to hand and add to it whenever you have another idea concerning accomplishments, skills, abilities and things that you enjoy or excel at. The key at this point is to be completely uncritical about the contents of your list and to work on it over a period of time. Even if you start off with a sense of inadequacy in the face of this task, you will soon surprise yourself with what a unique and gifted person you turn out to be.

An extract from your list might end up looking something like this:

- Voluntary work at a local hospice
- Research experience
- University hockey team

- Post-graduate degree
- 6 months teaching in India
- Counselling certificate/Uni NightOwls counselling team
- Bronze DofE Year 10...

Hopefully your list will be substantial if disorganised. Even an apparently trivial item may subsequently become useful.

While you are busy with this in your spare time, carry on reading this chapter. In a few days time, you will want to start converting your list into your personal statement.

What to Include

Even for the few schools who will not read your UCAS statement, your interviewers are likely to explore at least some if not all of the qualities that you should seek to include in your statement. Writing the statement may be your earliest chance to consider answers to fundamental questions. For this reason you will find some overlap between materials in this chapter and chapter 9 where interviews are discussed.

Why Medicine?

Some people find it easier to rephrase this question to 'When and how did you first become interested in medicine as a career?' It may be that you or someone important to you was very ill at some time in your past and the resultant experience of hospitals and doctors inspired you, perhaps you are already a healthcare professional wanting to advance your career, perhaps there was no defining moment, you just always wanted to do it. Whatever the case, you need to spend some time thinking about this aspect of your application. Avoid excuses for not having taken medicine as a school leaver, do not talk about what deterred you in the past, but explain what motivates you now.

Demonstrating Commitment

Although shadowing and wider reading each demonstrate a degree of commitment, the role of work experience cannot be overestimated. This topic is mentioned elsewhere in this book but it is such an important part of your personal statement that it is dealt with here as well. If you do not explain 'Why Medicine?' your application will probably still receive serious consideration. If you have no relevant work experience to talk about, it is unlikely that any schools will consider you further so in many respects the paragraphs on this topic are the most important of your statement.

The worst case is that you are reading this with either insignificant or non-existent work experience. You must organise something as a matter of urgency, not least because you are otherwise considering making one of the most important decisions of your life on less than adequate information. You must not lie on your application, do not pretend to have experience that you do not have and do not take the risk of writing about work experience that you have not yet organised as if it is something you have actually done, no matter how tempting. You will have to talk about this at interview and the interview panel is expert at spotting fabrications; they have heard it all before.

If you are or have ever worked as a healthcare professional, avoid detailed lists of your responsibilities – the reader will already know these – a very brief outline is all that is necessary. Focus instead on the personal qualities you have developed and used in this role. It will strengthen your statement further if you can provide evidence that you have expanded your experience in a different department or context from your usual responsibilities.

Ideally you will have a range of different experiences of working with people in a caring environment. In your final version you may not have room to provide more than a fairly bald list, but in your earliest drafts of your personal statement include things such as

- any specific responsibilities you had/have,
- what you learned (especially about yourself),
- how you feel about what you did,
- what was difficult,
- what you found especially rewarding and so on.

Keep these longer drafts as they will be useful if you are called to interview.

Demonstrating organisation skills and application

If you have outstanding academic results from both school and university but no extramural activities to describe, you have a problem. Think about times in your life when you were already heavily loaded with work and responsibilities (whether academically, professionally or personally) but undertook other activities as well. A job in the evenings or at weekends to finance your degree, for example, or active membership of a club which involved regular meetings and occupied time, would be good examples

Are you a 'well-rounded' person?

This overlaps, but is still distinct from, the question above about organisational skills. Because of the stressful nature of the training and career you are applying for, medical schools want you to have an outlet in the form of leisure activities. Think about how you spend your leisure time and how you can present this well in your personal statement. This should be an activity that is separate from voluntary work, required activities and so on; something that is purely for you – maybe you enjoy running or playing in a jazz band, for example. Note also that any extracurricular activity which is/was not obviously detrimental to your academic achievement or professional success will demonstrate that you are able to organise your workload efficiently and effectively.

Ideally, you should be able to give both physical and intellectual leisure activities but do not worry if your activities tend towards one or the other. Essentially, you should be doing something other than watching TV or going to the pub with your friends ('socialising') with at least some of your free time.

Demonstrating altruism?

This may well be demonstrated by your voluntary work, for example. It is altruistic to give up your free time to helping others for no reward (except that of being able to mention it on your UCAS form, of course!). One successful candidate described going swimming each week with a paraplegic friend who was only allowed in the pool if she had an able-bodied companion. Hopefully, you have something to offer in this respect.

Drafting Your Personal Statement

Look back at the list that you have made in your notebook and work experience diary. You will want to discard some things immediately. As much as possible, use recent or current examples of activities. Organise the remaining items under broad headings. Exactly what these are will depend on your list but will certainly include 'Work Experience', 'Leisure Activities' and so on. Once you have done this you are ready to start drafting your personal statement. Try to produce one or two paragraphs for each heading. Do not worry about length at this point unless you find that you have little to say.

If your list is still worryingly short, now is the time to get friends to help out. You will get a better and more constructive response from almost everyone you ask if, instead of telling them that you want a list of things for your UCAS form, you ask 'What qualities do I have that make me unique?' Hopefully what they have to say about you will give you a few more ideas for yourself.

Dealing with negative content

Everyone will have weaknesses and gaps in their application. As a generalisation you should avoid highlighting these – if they matter that much, the schools to which you are applying will identify them anyway and you are wasting valuable words.

A common concern amongst graduate applicants is that of dismal A-level results. Medicine is an academically demanding course and A-level grades for school leavers are set correspondingly high. Poor performance in A-levels may well be the reason why you did not study medicine as your first degree. You must highlight your academic achievement since then. Remember that graduate entry courses are in part designed to widen access and many schools have already made the decision to ignore A-level results.

If you are still at university and so have no qualifications more recent than your A-levels, you should probably mention academic ability in some way. First and foremost, do not bother with excuses. Whatever the reason for your lack of effort, you got poor A-level results because you did not do the necessary work. Accept this brutal fact and move on. Your strength lies in the fact that you have changed the way you work as a result of your poor showing at A-level. You could say something like, 'studying at degree level has taught me how to organise my work load efficiently and to apply myself effectively to my work.' Acknowledgement of your inadequate A-levels is implied rather than explicit but, more importantly, you have shown yourself as someone who can modify their approach to a key area of their life.

If you have a weakness that you really feel you cannot avoid mentioning, try to treat it in a similar way and turn it into a strength.

The Style of your Statement

If you are lucky, your personal statement will be the first one the Admissions Tutor reads after coffee on Monday morning. If you are not, yours will be the last one he reads before tea on Friday afternoon. What makes your personal statement eye catching enough to be worth a closer look and maybe even an offer of an interview?

For example, 'At Primary school I was an elf in the Woodcraft Folk and particularly enjoyed camping and bivouacking' will certainly catch the eye of anyone reading your personal statement, but probably will not have quite the impact you were hoping for. It also begs the question; if you enjoyed it that much why do you not have a more recent example of the outdoor life to describe?

Alternatively, 'to fund my studies, I work as a juggler and fire-eater in a circus, in the evening shows, in the matinee performances at the weekend and full time during my vacations' (if true, of course), is not only eye-catching in itself as a fairly unusual skill and experience but also implies that you are working during term time and hence adds evidence for an ability to organise your work load efficiently.

Some people pick a slightly unconventional style of presentation for their statement as a means of capturing attention. Included later is an example of this sort of approach. This technique can work well but needs to be used with caution. Remember, your personal statement makes your first impression for you; be aware of this aspect of your statement when revising it.

Similarly, some sources of advice suggest that bullet points might be a useful approach to the restricted space of the personal statement, this approach may not be appropriate here. Firstly, bullet points are neither easier to read nor less demanding of space than a piece of continuous prose. Secondly, one of the skills that medical schools are interested in is your communication skills. A straightforward piece of writing with a restricted word count on a specified subject is an excellent test of basic communications skills. Make sure you pass this one with flying colours.

Revising your first draft

Go back to the websites and prospectuses for your chosen schools and find a list of things they are looking for in applicants. Compare this list to your personal statement – have you included everything they are looking for? If not, go back to your initial list, did you leave something helpful out? Add in the necessary material to your draft to satisfy all specified requirements.

Read over your text looking for any repetition of information that is found elsewhere on the form and remove it. The sole exception to this should be relevant work experience.

Get a red pen or a highlighter pen and mark every occurrence of the word 'I' and look for alternative ways of beginning sentences to get rid of all but one or two beginning 'I'. Then look for alternative vocabulary for words you have repeated noticeably.

Further Revisions

The second version may be longer than your first if you have added in more material to satisfy specifics for one or more institutions. Read through carefully and start to get a feel for whether or not you have placed the emphasis correctly. Listing modules from your degree, for example, is of minimal value and interest; that one sentence you put in about spending last summer working for Riding for the Disabled says far more of importance about you and deserves expansion.

If you are content that the emphasis and balance of the various elements is about right, start to think about word count. You should be aiming for around 550 words for your statement to fill the space provided neatly but without looking too crowded. You will probably find that the statement is far too long so you need to get really ruthless at this point.

Look for material that you can omit without leaving a significant gap in your presentation. Look for rambling and unfocused sentences and tighten up your use of language. Generally, try to use strong, positive sentences. Keep reducing the content until the word count is approximately correct (550 words).

The Opening Statement

Do you have a strong opening sentence or paragraph? Now is the time to really think about this. If you can get this right you will make an immediate, positive impact on your reader. Some successful, graduate entry applicants have agreed that we can quote from their personal statements. Here are the opening 100 – 200 words from a selection of these. Look at each of these statements critically. What makes them strong? What weakens them in your opinion?

Example 1:

I am a practising State Registered Paramedic, currently employed by the Tees, East and North Yorkshire Ambulance Service NHS Trust. Prior to this I have worked in similar roles for other NHS ambulance services.

I am now reaching the limit of clinical development available to me within my current profession but I wish to continue to advance and mature as a practitioner and a healthcare professional. It is important to me that I can continue to work with people and I feel that I can best realise my own potential and also maximise the level of care that I am able to offer to patients by retraining as a doctor.

This is very good. A strong opening consisting of a clear but brief description of the author's current role and then a good rationale for retraining to be a doctor.

Example 2:

After working in management consultancy for five years, I have decided that I want to pursue a career in a caring profession. The primary reason is that, whilst I have enjoyed my job and been successful, I have found my voluntary activities in caring roles to be far more fulfilling. I have worked university holidays as a nurse in elderly and psychiatric wards, volunteered for a year at a weekend session for mentally ill individuals, and have spent the last 9 months volunteering at a London hospital on the elderly and now the admissions ward.

This is a weak opening statement – the author's job and years of employment are elsewhere on the form. They would get a better starting point if they began 'Whilst I have enjoyed my job…etc'. University holidays were at least 5 year ago. Although very useful and relevant, they should have focused attention onto the more recent experiences and given the old stuff a much less prominent position.

Example 3:

Having a physiology degree and full time employment experience within a hospital environment I have decided to pursue a career in medicine. I feel that my academic and work experience has given me a true idea about the realities of studying for and pursuing a career in medicine, which may not have been apparent at a younger age. I gained a II.i in my physiology degree, modules included; metabolic, renal, exercise, CNS and reproductive physiology. My dissertation consisted of a literature review regarding the physiological mechanisms of pain relief and a research project evaluating the effect of age on left ventricular hypertrophy. In September 2004 I qualified as a Donor Care Physiologist at Papworth Hospital, Cambridge.

Rather weak. Much of the statement consisted of detailed lists similar to the ones shown above. Most of the material was irrelevant to their application and the important and relevant information buried under a mass of detail.

Example 4:

This is something that I have always wanted to do since I was a child, and if it were not for a change of rules that meant I could not study biology in my final years at school, I would probably be a doctor now. I have been successful in many other fields - as a scientist, businesswoman, economist and musician, but I always promised myself that when my children were settled at school full-time I would fill the gap in my life sciences and apply to medical college. I am now studying biology and chemistry A-levels full time and I have never been happier. I have also had the good fortune to be able to shadow three GP's and one consultant, confirming my ambition to be an inner-city GP. I grew up surrounded by medicine (my grandmother was a GP and my grandfather a general surgeon) so I am very well aware of the commitment and deep sense of social responsibility that is needed in this profession.

The opening is weakened by beginning with an excuse. Emphasising the large number of roles they have had can be interpreted as lacking 'staying power'– a bit of a butterfly. In addition, the information is too densely packed – there is material for three paragraphs here.

Example 5:
Having been the sort of child who felt compelled, from an early age, to bandage her friends, rescue sick animals and avidly view TV hospital dramas, it was assumed by myself and my family that entering medicine was a foregone conclusion. However, the plans were somewhat disrupted by a sustained period of teenage rebellion, resulting in lower than expected O-level results. A-levels came to a sticky end at about the same time as my long-term boyfriend and two close family members. It was then I decided to take it easy with a medical secretarial course instead, and indulge in some essential paid employment, with the intention of resuming studies and attempting entrance to medical school when I felt better. During my second attempt at A-levels, I found myself unexpectedly pregnant, and decided I should do the decent thing and marry the father. Which, with hindsight, was a mistake because he was less than enthusiastic about my plans for world domination through medicine, and insisted that I settle for a quiet job as a

secretary. I considered it a sensible option, as money was so scarce I could
not afford to give up work and study anyway.

The use of a very informal style grabs the attention of the reader and
their resilient, bubbly character shines through. However, the impact is
marred by excuses.

Example 6:

I first became interested in a career in medicine when working in a boarding
school. For two years I was responsible for Sick Wing during Matron's days
off and during her sometimes protracted absences due to ill health.   I
routinely dealt with minor injuries and illnesses, liasing with the school GP
or arranging for pupils to be taken to A&E if necessary.   I was also
responsible for administering non-prescription drugs and ensuring detailed
accurate records were maintained.

Too old to be considered for medical school at that time, I was still interested
in a career in science. I took two A levels in one academic year, relying on
independent study because I was in a full time, resident post.

The opening paragraph is a straightforward description of relevant work
experience and begins to answer 'why medicine?' even though this is
some time in the past (as would be apparent from the work record – it is
not necessary to highlight the timescale at this point on the form). The
mention of extra A-levels and the circumstances under which they were
taken in this case illustrates that the candidate has the motivation and
discipline to study.

The Final Stages

Once you are comfortable with your personal statement, check the
character count – your statement should be less than 4,000 characters in

length.   Paste it into your application form; it should automatically reformat itself to the required font and font size.   Check carefully that your full text fits into the allocated space; as well as a limit on the number of characters, a maximum of only 50 lines are allowed.   If your full text does not fit in spite of containing fewer than 4,000 characters, you may need to reduce the number of lines either by deleting empty lines between paragraphs or by linking two or more paragraphs together to make a single, longer paragraph.

Finally, check for adjacent lines beginning with the same word.   The eye easily jumps a line under these circumstances and the reader may omit important information as a result.   Restructure this part of your statement if necessary to avoid the problem.

Finally, do you like what you see?   Are you happy for complete strangers to base their assumptions about you on this statement?

If so, ensure you have completed the rest of the form and then submit it.

Remember to make a printout of the final version of your personal statement so that you can refer to it when preparing for interviews.

Summary

DO NOT

- Make excuses
- Make errors in spelling and grammar
- Suggest that your current role is boring
- Repeat information found elsewhere on the form
- Overcrowd the space
- Dwell on the past

DO

- Make a strong opening statement
- Use clear, positive language throughout
- Focus on personal development
- Concentrate on the present
- Give a clear description of relevant work experience

Entrance Exams

The government drive for more doctors and wider access to medicine has resulted in new medical schools, new graduate entry courses and revised selection procedures. The increasingly large volume of applications, formulaic personal statements, high grades and lack of confidentiality with respect to references has made selecting candidates for interview increasingly difficult for all medical courses.

Amongst graduates, the age of applicants varies by over 20 years and many schools feel that the academic ability of such a variety of applicants cannot be measured by degree alone. The potential of a 21-year-old biochemistry graduate is incomparable with that of a 37-year-old lawyer. Entrance exams go some way towards levelling the playing field. For some people, the fact that their first class degree in biomedical sciences is almost irrelevant (for some schools) may be a source of frustration. However, schools also hope to test skills and attitudes that are not directly measured in A-levels or undergraduate degree results.

Entry requirements for graduate entry programmes vary between schools. Some schools feel that graduates of all disciplines should have the opportunity to apply, whilst others do not. Study of the humanities has been shown to correlate with better clinical performance, but scientific knowledge is core to a medical degree. Most schools accepting an arts degree test science in their entrance exam. However, King's College, Leicester, Newcastle and Southampton are notable in that they neither require a science degree, nor test science directly, as they use the UKCAT exam. However, whilst UKCAT does not test science as such, the responses given highlight whether the candidate has an aptitude for the logical reasoning and interpersonal skills required as a student and as a clinician.

Amongst the three exams, there is a predominance of multiple choice questions (MCQs). BMAT also uses extended matching questions (EMQs) and short answer questions (SAQs).

Please see Chapter 3 for entry requirements and statistics for each individual school.

Note that you must register for these exams in addition to the usual application to UCAS.

UKCAT   www.ukcat.ac.uk

Imperial, King's, Leicester, Newcastle, Oxford, Queen's, Southampton & Warwick require UKCAT for their graduate entry medicine courses.

UKCAT is an aptitude test. Held in over 150 test centres around the world, candidates will be tested at a computer terminal. The test takes 2 hours, and results are available immediately. A candidate's score can therefore guide their university choices prior to application to UCAS.

However, most schools will not advise on scores needed, not least because it is only one of a number of variables, and a relatively new and untested one at that. To guide you, King's are likely to select from the 25th centile, Oxford are likely to require scores of greater than 600 in all sections and Warwick will select from at least the 50th centile. For 2009 entry, Queens considered applicants with scores above 2450.

In 2007, 15730 people took the exam for entry to medicine (undergraduate and graduate courses), with mean scores as follows:

	Mean	Maximum available
Verbal Reasoning	593	900
Quantitative Reasoning	639	900
Abstract Reasoning	598	900
Decision Analysis	600	900
Total	**2430**	**3600**

There is no more information available to guide students as to the scores needed, but it stands to reason that you should aim to score above average. Most medical students are, essentially, above average people!

The UKCAT is £60 for candidates taking the test in the EU before 31st August 2009, and £95 for other candidates. Between the 1st September and 9th October 2009, the cost is £75 for candidates taking the UKCAT in the EU. Book early, but note that you can only book a maximum of 90 days in advance. It is possible to obtain a bursary for the UKCAT, although you must apply for it before you sit the test.

Candidates applying for 2010 entry or deferred entry in 2011 must take the UKCAT before 9th October 2009. UKCAT results are only valid for applications which are made in the year in which the test is taken.

UKCAT Structure

5 subtests of Multiple Choice Questions (MCQs):

There is no curriculum or science content for UKCAT, but consists of reasoning and analysis. The examiners are testing skills and behaviours that identify candidates as having potential in a later medical career:

- Verbal reasoning (44 items) Assesses candidates' ability to think logically about written information & arrive at a reasoned conclusion
- Quantitative reasoning (40 items) Assesses candidates' ability to solve numerical problems
- Abstract reasoning (65 items) Assesses candidates' ability to infer relationships from information by convergent and divergent thinking
- Decision analysis (26 items) assesses candidates' ability to deal with various forms of information, to infer relationships, to make informed judgements, and to decide on an appropriate response, in situations of complexity and ambiguity.
- Non-cognitive analysis - identifies the attributes and characteristics of robustness, empathy and integrity that may contribute to successful health professional practice.

UKCAT Section by Section

    1)   *Verbal reasoning*

This subtest looks at 11 passages, each with 4 statements i.e. 44 test items. There are 22 minutes for this subtest, so you need to allow no more than 2 minutes for each passage (30secs per question). Each statement has 3 answer options; True, False, or Can't Tell. 'True' means that the statement is either in the passage or follows logically from it; 'False' means that the statement directly contradicts the passage, or logically contradicts it; and 'Can't Tell' means that you have insufficient information as to whether the statement is true or false.

The passages in question are taken from newspapers, magazines etc. Ignore your prior knowledge, only use the passage, and draw conclusions only from the information contained therein. It is possible that a passage will contain information which you know is wrong; this does not matter, concentrate on the passage and its information only.

    2)   *Quantitative Reasoning*

This subtest contains 10 tables, charts, and/or graphs, each with 4 MCQs. Each MCQ has 5 options, and you are allowed to use a calculator. You are allowed 22 minutes for this subtest.

The level required is GCSE Maths, but you need to problem-solve, and manipulate the information using simple calculations and ratios.

- Addition, subtraction, multiplication and division.
- Interpretation of histograms, graphs, pie charts, tables etc
- Calculation and estimation of means, medians, ranges, quartiles
- Fractions, decimals, and percentages, and their manipulation
- Conversion of measurements and units
- Use of formulae & equations, and their basic rearrangement
- Powers, square roots, proportion & ratio calculation

It is not inconceivable that you have not seen a calculator since GCSE/O-level, so familiarise yourself with it and the maths above. Read the information carefully; the calculations themselves are relatively easy.

3)   *Abstract Reasoning*

Here there are 13 pairs of sets of shapes, each of which has 5 MCQs associated with it. For each question, you are shown a 'test shape', and asked whether this relates best to Set A, Set B, or neither. You are allowed 16 minutes for this subtest.

This is a pattern recognition exercise. There is a method to the examiners' madness, and there will be a logical pattern underpinning the question. There are only a limited number of ways in which the examiner can change these shapes, so be systematic in your approach.

In Set A & Set B, think about:
- How many shapes there are?
- Are there general shapes (e.g. curved) or specific ones (e.g. stars)?
- Their colour, and how the colours relate to each other
- Their size, and any variation in size
- What do they look like; round, straight, pointy, open-ended, a shape within a shape, dotted lines, squares, triangles, pentagons etc.?
- How many sides do they have?
- Have they been rotated or reflected at all?
- Are they distributed across the box in a certain way, i.e. in opposition to each other, close to the edge, all on the right hand side etc.?
- Irrelevant and distracting material may also have been included.

Many people find this section some kind of Machiavellian torture. The trick is to get used to the questions. There is mindset for this section, and practice is the best way to tackle it.

4)   *Decision Analysis*

In this subtest, there are 26 MCQs relating to a scenario, and each containing 4 or 5 response options. You are allowed 30 minutes for this subtest. Please note that more than one of the options could be correct, in which case you should identify all the correct options available.

The scenarios have introductory text, followed by a code-key table. The questions require the deciphering of phrases using this table, so if $ is cold, and ! is rain, then $! becomes snow.

This is a test of judgement, rather than the use of any prior knowledge. The basic code-key table is provided for each question, with a link back to the introductory information should you need it. The questions will become increasingly ambiguous, with more complex information, although in reality this simply means additional code-key tables. Judgement will be most needed when combining words to make new meaning; e.g. adding 'opposite' to 'worry' means 'enjoy'. It will also be needed when several answers are possible, but there should be one (or if specified two) which clearly fit best. Note also the order of the code, since this will change meanings. Examiners may alternatively give a meaning and asking you to provide the code for it.

5)   *Non-Cognitive Analysis*

UKCAT do not think it appropriate to use these results in selection until there is evidence to support a relationship between the test results and success of a student or doctor. It is possible that the information could be used as part of mentoring students when at university. There is no right or wrong answer to the questions. Some candidates worry that this is all a massive conspiracy, and that their answer could jeopardise their chances. This is not true, and the message should be to answer the questions honestly, and to not worry.

Preparation for UKCAT

Although the organisers of the exam say that you cannot revise for it, you can definitely prepare for it. You need to familiarise yourself with the style and content of the exam and then gain sufficient relevant practice in each of the sections.

- Official example questions available can be found at www.ukcat.ac.uk The exam is computerised, and you must familiarise yourself with the format. Example questions found there also have the answers, and their underlying rationale. The hints and tips are also useful.

- Googling UKCAT will unearth many different companies who offer practice at varying prices, but why not do the free stuff first! :

- Google 'online aptitude tests', and do them ALL, they are all useful practice. UKCAT is similar to the Civil Service exams, and various other graduate recruitment exams. For instance:

- www.shldirect.com

- www.savilleconsulting.com/products/aptitude_preparationguides.aspx

- www.psl.com

- practicetests.cubiks.com

- www.previsor.co.uk

- www.kent.ac.uk/careers/tests/verbaltest.htm.

- BMAT and UKCAT Uncovered: A guide to medical school entrance exams by T. O. Osinowo, R. A. Weerakkody & H. W. Woodward

- Passing the UK Clinical Aptitude Test and BMAT by Rosalie Hutton, Glenn Hutton, Felicity Walker also has a section on BMAT.

- Barrett, Jim (2002) How To Pass Advanced Aptitude Tests

- Bryon, Mike (2005) Graduate Psychometric Test Workbook

- Shavick, Andrea (2005) Practice Psychometric Tests

- Practice section 1 of the GAMSAT and BMAT exam sample papers

- You can sharpen your diagrammatic reasoning ability by doing abstract or shape-based puzzles in newspapers and magazines.

Hints and Tips for the UKCAT exam

- There is no negative marking in this exam. Do not leave blanks.

- Re-read the instructions for each section the night before to reduce the chance of panic in the exam.

- Pace yourself. Know how many minutes are available for question and use the onscreen clock.

- Do not stall on a question. You can mark a question for review at the end, which enables you to click on a link to take you back to that question. Mark down an answer anyway, in case you do not have the opportunity to return.

- When guessing any answers, ensure that you increase your chances of success by first eliminating wrong answers.

- Many teachers recommend reading the questions before the passage. Practice this technique and see if it works for you.

- In a previous exam, candidates were unable to progress to the next question because the scroll bar had not reached the end of this page. Whilst this particular glitch should be fixed, shocks can be avoided by practicing questions on the UKCAT website.

- See general tips on MCQs & EMQs at the end of this chapter.

GAMSAT   www.gamsatuk.org

The Graduate Australian Medical School Admissions Test (GAMSAT) is a graduate entrance exam used by Nottingham, St. George's, Swansea and Keele for their graduate entry programme, and by Peninsula for their standard entry course for graduates who took their A-levels more than 2 years ago.

It is a demanding pen and paper test, which takes place in a number of test centres around the country. The test last all day, and candidates need to report at about 8a.m. There is a lunch break, and a lot of hanging around. The purpose of the exam is to assess a candidate's ability to understand and analyse material, to think critically about issues and, in the written section, to organise and express thoughts in a logical and effective way. The emphasis is on problem-solving, and on the interpretation of information and applied reasoning.

GAMSAT costs £192 to register before 5pm on 14th August 2009. After that, but before 5pm on 28th August 2009, it will cost an additional £50. At this point registration is closed. Please note that if you purchase the official GAMSAT practice tests and questions cost an additional £58.

The GAMSAT exam will be held on 18th September 2009 and its results are valid for 2 years. This sitting is the only occasion when GAMSAT can be sat in the UK, although it is also held in Ireland in March. GAMSAT centres are located in Bristol, Swansea, London, Nottingham, Sheffield and Melbourne (Australia). Centres are filled on a first come first served basis. Results are released after about 7 weeks.

GAMSAT Structure & Marking

GAMSAT consists of 3 sections. Each section is separately timed, and total test time is 5½ hours spread over approximately 8 hours. Non-programmable calculators are allowed.

- I – Reasoning in Humanities and Social Sciences
- II – Written Communication
- III – Reasoning in Biological and Physical Sciences

Each of the sections is marked out of 100, and the overall mark is calculated using the following formula:

Overall Score = (1 x Section I + 1 x Section II + 2 x Section III) ÷ 4

Schools interpret the results of GAMSAT differently.

To be considered for St. George's or Nottingham, candidates have to achieve a competitive average score and also need to obtain a minimum score of 55 in Section II, and 55 in either Section I or Section III with a minimum of 50 in the other section. For Keele, the overall GAMSAT score needed for interview in 2008 was either 55% average (section I, II and III minimums of 50, 50 and 60) or 60% average (section I, II and III minimums of 50, 50 and 55). Peninsula thresholds may differ from this.

GAMSAT Section by Section

  1)   Section I – Reasoning in Humanities & Social Sciences
100 minutes, 75 MCQs.

This section requires candidates to interpret information, which can take the form of written prose, pictures, cartoons, tables and graphs. For example official example questions include building plans and a guide on how to tie knots! This section is not a test of knowledge, so use the information in the passage only to draw your conclusions. If you happen to know that information in the passage is wrong, assume that it is correct for the purposes of the exam.

The examiners are testing not only your interpretational skills, including logic & critical thinking, but also your interpersonal skills, such as empathy. Acknowledge any positive or negative feelings that you have, as these may be the feelings that the author is trying to evoke, and which the examiners are trying to test.

2)   Section II – Written Communication

60 minutes, two written essays, with 5 minutes reading time

This section assesses writing ability with a special emphasis on the thoughts and ideas contained in candidates' written responses. Test A is an objective essay dealing with current affairs & socio-cultural issues, and calls for expository and argumentative writing. Test B is a reflective essay dealing with more interpersonal and intrapersonal issues, and calls for personal and discursive writing. In both scenarios, you will be presented with a number of quotes relating to a theme. The candidate can respond to 1 or more of the quotes.

A number of criteria are used to mark essays. The first is the thought and content; the quality of what is said. The examiners will look at what answer is constructed and developed from the task and the kinds of thoughts and feelings that are offered in response. The second criterion is the organisation and expression of your writing, looking at the structure that has developed in terms of its form and layout, and the language used in terms of fluency, coherence and clarity. You will need to maintain acceptable spelling and grammar too. Each essay is assessed by 3 independent markers.

Take 7 to 10 minutes to plan your essay. The first step is to decide how to treat the quotes that you are faced with, so read them all carefully twice. You can pick one quote and wax lyrical solely about this or you can pick two to compare and contrast, or more if you so choose. There is no right or wrong number of quotes to use. Once you have decided on your quote(s), write ideas down either as notes, or better still as a diagrammatic plan. Identify that what you have scrawled is a plan, or indeed cross it out if necessary, as it will be handed in to the examiners.

When planned properly, your essay is ready to write. Make sure that you include an introduction and a conclusion. Try to go into the exam with a clear skeleton for an essay structure already in your head. Structure is very important in essay writing, such that arguments are logically ordered and examiners find it easy to follow.

Try to back up all arguments with an example, and that your argument is relevant to the quote(s) you are responding to. For each writing task, a maximum of 3 arguments with associated example would seem reasonable, plus a suitable introduction and conclusion. In essence, stay relevant to the subject at hand, try to be balanced in your reasoning, focus on quality not quantity, and don't forget your introduction or conclusion.

A final point regarding the essay is to watch your timing. It is easy to spend 5 minutes too long on the first essay to make it really good, but then you will have hardly any time to write your second. Each are worth the same amount of marks, so give them the equal time. You are unlikely to gain as many additional marks in 5 extra minutes on one essay as you will relinquish in the 5 minutes lost on the other.

3)   Section III – Reasoning in Biological and Physical Sciences

170 minutes, 110 MCQs.

This section tests problem-solving in a scientific context, in addition to recall and understanding of the basic scientific concepts that a candidate would be expected to know at the start of a medical course.

It is made up of questions in three areas:

- Chemistry (40% of the exam)
- Biology (40% of the exam)
- Physics (20% of the exam)

This section tends to cause the greatest concern amongst candidates. The thought of doing 110 questions in 3 hours to a relatively high standard of science puts many off the GAMSAT entirely. However, more people fail the essay section than the science section, and many arts graduates have succeeded in this science section, so you need to appreciate that it is achievable.

GAMSATUK suggest that candidates acquire a level of knowledge consistent with first year degree level in biology and chemistry, and A-level physics. However, in reality, if you are proficient in these sciences at A-level, then you should be capable of achieving the marks required, especially when you consider that degrees vary hugely, with many limiting the first year to A-level standard. Note that you are allowed to use a non-programmable calculator in this section.

Realise early that you should not attempt to learn the whole of A-level Biology, Chemistry and Physics. In fact, avoid rote learning, and focus instead on *understanding* the science, so that you are able to apply it when necessary. Year after year the same themes and types of questions come up. If you look at the practice papers supplied by UCAS, then you will be able to see the themes too. We have outlined them in the preparation section.

General Preparation for GAMSAT

Familiarity is more likely to result in understanding and skill than a last minute cram. There is no safe answer to the question 'do I need to know this?' The more reading you do, the better prepared you will be. Also, no knowledge is a waste, and any learning will be useful at medical school.

You must obtain the practice papers from UCAS, these cost £58 and are available from www.gamsatuk.org. These have not changed for years (apart from the colour of the cover) so you can buy second hand copies with confidence. Out of the 3 booklets available, only one has worked answers. You will also not be able to get any real insight into how the writing tasks are marked. Unfortunately, if you want to practice more, then there is a real dearth of practice questions for free online.

There are a number of companies that offer a number of preparation courses and practice papers, which vary in length (and cost) according to your needs. We would recommend that you delay booking these until you discover how much help you need, by buying the official preparation papers and following the section specific advice below. Then, if you attend a course, you will already know your areas of weakness, and can concentrate on these during the course. The more work you do beforehand, the more you will get out of any course.

There are a number of text books which you may find useful, and some are detailed below.

A good starting point, which covers all the sections of GAMSAT is one of the Medical College Admission Test (MCAT) guides. MCAT is an exam taken by medical school applicants in the USA. Although not specific to any UK entrance exam, many of the skills tested in the MCAT exam are very similar to those tested in GAMSAT. Note that MCAT candidates necessarily have a science degree and there is an emphasis on knowledge rather than just understanding. Note also that spelling and some terminology can be different in the US. However, these books cover natural sciences, maths, verbal reasoning and written communication. You can acquire cheap copies on Ebay.

GAMSAT Section by Section Preparation

1)   Preparation for GAMSAT Section I

Practice is the only way to succeed.

Suggested Reading for Reasoning

- MCAT preparation as detailed above
- A tutorial in critical reasoning:
  commhum.mccneb.edu/argument/summary.htm
- Practice the verbal reasoning questions for UKCAT and for section 1 of BMAT

2)   Preparation for GAMSAT Section II

The purpose of the essay is to see whether you can assemble a set of ideas in a coherent manner in a short space of time.

Whatever the type of essay, there are three parts to a successful essay: planning, paragraphing and sticking to the point. Remember, you only have 30 minutes for the essay.

Writing two half hour essays concurrently is actually physically difficult for the majority of people who have become reliant on computers and so you really must practice repeatedly under timed conditions. The essay quotes can seem quite abstract. In addition, many candidates find it quite unnerving to write reflectively about themselves.

Practice planning essays, so that you are comfortable with them, and being able to transcribe them into a coherent essay. For further practice, look at practice papers, and you should be able to find essay titles online and in forums. Keep abreast of current medical issues, ethics and developments as this could provide you with examples in your essay, and may also be useful for interviews too. Remember that neater essays are easier to mark and to read.

Here are some suggestions for improving your essay writing technique:

- MCAT preparation as detailed above
- Eira Makepeace, Writing Essays for GAMSAT (Spine Publishing) is soon to be published and includes essays written by successful candidates
- There are more ideas about essay writing on some of the forums, for instance the 'essay writing for GAMSAT' section at www.medschoolguide.co.uk. Note that the postings are subjective opinions and may not always be accurate - you must use a critical eye.
- A simple clear approach is found in Derek Rowntree, Learn How to Study: a realistic approach 4th edition (Warner, 1998)
- See also Flesch, Rudolph; Lass, A.H., A Classic Guide to Better Writing (New York: Harper, 1966) and make sure you have the latest edition.

3) Preparation for GAMSAT Section III

Remember that the key is to understand topics, so that you can apply them to the information given. For example, no one will ask you to recite the Kreb's cycle, but you may be asked to answer questions based on a given diagram or information about it.

You may wish to ensure that you understand the following science areas:

Biology:

Essentially anything that relates to human biology, including:

- Prokaryotic and eukaryotic cells
- Cell structure, including cell life cycle (meiosis vs. mitosis), metabolism (including aerobic vs. anaerobic)
- The different kinds of movement at a cellular level, including osmosis, passive & active transport, and facilitated diffusion
- DNA, RNA and protein synthesis
- Genetics, including Mendelian genetics and Punnett's Squares
- Enzymes and their control, protein structure and function
- Reproductive system
- Basic embryology
- Nerves, including their relation to muscle contraction
- Endocrinology
- Circulation, including the structure & physiology of the heart, blood pressure & factors that influence it, and the blood's constituents (including the immune system & clotting factors)
- Respiratory, including oxygen & carbon dioxide transportation, dissociation curves, haemoglobin and myoglobin
- The Gastrointestinal tract, and its regulation
- Renal system, including kidney structure and function
- The eye and the ear

- Animal disease, and immune response to this
- Population dynamics, e.g. of bacteria
- Scientific techniques, including chromatography, titres, bacterial culturing etc.

Chemistry:

Concepts here relate to both inorganic and organic chemistry, including:

- Structure of atoms, including: protons, neutrons & electrons, mass & atomic numbers, electronegativity & electron orbitals.
- Bonding and structure
- Basic concentration calculations and molar calculations
- Molecules, including: bonding types, representation of molecules on paper, structural isomerism, empirical formulae, reaction types (redox, hydration, hydrolysis, dehydration, hydrogenation), stereoisomerism, different types of organic molecule (alcohols, esters etc.), electronic resonance, aromativity, intermolecular interactions, factors affecting melting and boiling points
- Thermodynamics, including: entropy, enthalpy, Gibbs energy, activation energy, reaction profiles
- Acids & Bases, including: Definition of pH & pKa, weak vs strong acid, buffering
- Equilibria, including: concept of dynamic equilibrium, equilibrium constant and how to produce one
- Reaction kinetics, including: rate equations, orders of reaction, rate constants
- Redox reactions, including: half reactions, electronic cells, oxidation numbers, definition of oxidation & reduction, standard electrode potentials
- Solutions, including: solvents, solutes, solubility, saturation, factors that affect solubility

Physics:

There is a much smaller pool of knowledge required for Physics, which reflects the smaller amount of marks available:

- Mechanics: Linear motion, velocity, Force, weight, mass and acceleration (including gravity), Moments, Density, Energy and Force, including gravitational potential energy & kinetic energy, Torque and its relationship to force & its magnitude, Angular acceleration

- Electric and magnetic fields: Electric field concepts, Electric field strength and influence on charged particles, Magnetic field concepts, Magnetic field strength and influence on charged particles

- Electronics: Capacitance, Resistance, changes in these when circuits are in parallel or series, current and voltage, the relationship between current and voltage, induction of electric charge

- Optics and Waves: Thin lenses, including fields, diffraction and refraction, esp applied to the eye, the relationship between velocity, wavelength and frequency

- Physics interacting with Maths: rearranging equations, applying logic, density, relationship between volume & mass

Mathematics

There are no outlined marks for Maths in this paper, but in order to maximise your marks, you will need to know about the following:

- Data interpretation, manipulation & analysis, including of graphs, pie charts, histograms, logarithms, charts and tables
- Conversion of units, and assessment of magnitude

- Equation rearrangement, and ratio calculation
- Basic trigonometry
- Population calculations
- Interpretation of patterns

These lists are certainly not exhaustive. Equally, do not let the size of them scare you; you do not have to memorise great reams of knowledge to do well in this exam. For instance, a question a few years ago asked the candidate to apply physics concepts of acceleration to the gait of a dinosaur. You would never have learnt about how Tyrannosaurus Rex prepares for the marathon, but by being familiar with the concepts above, and by not being scared of them, you should be able to see which multiple choice options are definitely wrong, and hopefully calculate which ones are right.

Suggested Reading

The topics listed above are covered in the following suggested reading:

- MCAT resources as described above
- Oxford Revision Guides; AS+A-Level;

    www.oup.com/oxed/secondary/revision

    - very clear, with simple diagrams

    - the human biology book includes material used in first year graduate medicine

    - the physics book has a useful medical physics section

- Revision Express; A-Level Study Guide (AS+A2);

    www.revision-express.com

    - slightly more wordy and more basic content than Oxford Revision Guides

    - excellent format of one topic per page

- Letts Educational; A2 Level; www.letts-education.com

- colourful and clear
- great diagrams
- excellent answer explanations
- Make the Grade; AS+A2 Revision Guide;
  www.nelsonthornes.com
  - simple style
- Exam Revision Notes; AS/A-Level; www.philipallan.co.uk
  - very basic with minimal explanations
  - revision notes only
- Basic Science Internet guides.
  - Google 'biology online', 'chemistry online' etc
  - Many sites are rather gimmicky, but they are a great resource for people feeling a little overwhelmed by the whole science issue. Also, they can be great for dipping into for just 10 minutes a day at work.

GAMSAT Hints & Tips

- Keep to time. In Section I, there is 1 minute 20s per question, for Section III, there is 1 minute 32s per question, and half an hour for each essay.
- Many questions used in GAMSAT are test questions for the following year. This is the reason why many of your questions will differ from your neighbours'. These test questions will not be marked. If you dwell on a question, it could be one that will not be marked, and may contain mistakes!
- If you really find yourself spending too long on a question, take a guess, and move on.
- Practice UKCAT and BMAT sample papers as the skills tested are not mutually exclusive.
- There is no negative marking in the multiple choice questions, so try not to leave anything blank. When the author of the chapter

invigilated, it was noticeable how many people left sections blank. You have a 1 in 4 chance if you guess. It won't feel like it, but it could be your lucky day!

- Eliminate incorrect answers first to improve these odds.

- Sections I & III are marked by a computer, so be careful to rub out any mistakes completely. If the computer interprets two pencil marks for any question, then it will mark it wrong.

- Each multiple choice question only requires one answer.

- Scribble, underline and calculate to heart's content. This can make it easier if you need to come back to a question later on.

- Keep your essay neat, and cross out your essay plan.

- Ignore anyone else that is scribbling furiously whilst apparently composing War & Peace and asking for more paper. They are not doing your paper, you are.

- Ditto the above for anyone that finishes early, sits around looking bored, cries, sleeps or starts to pray. When the author of the chapter took GAMSAT, there was an awful lot of rumour mongering going on in the queue. It was all false, and you are best to ignore it.

- The information needed to answer the question is usually provided, so check the question again if you are really stuck.

- GAMSAT is notoriously tough; and others will have found it this way too.

- It can be cold in the exam hall, so take extra layers.

- Be prepared for sitting in a hall with thousands of people!

- Take a packed lunch, it is no longer included in the £192 fee.

- See also the general tips at the end of this chapter.

BMAT   www.bmat.org.uk

There is no graduate course for which the Biomedical Admission Test (BMAT) is essential. It is used for a small number of undergraduate courses, including Cambridge, Imperial College London, Oxford, and UCL. Applicants for the Cambridge Graduate course 'can use a successful result as part of their pre-medical requirements'. Note that you will need to apply for the exam separately from your UCAS application.

BMAT consists of three discrete components, with a total test time of 2 hours designed to assess performance in the areas of:
- Aptitude and skills (35 MCQs and SAQs in 60 minutes)
- Scientific knowledge and application (27 MCQs & SAQs in 30 mins)
- Written task (1 essay in 30 minutes)

The BMAT, held on 4th November 2009, is £32.10 for a UK candidate. There are higher costs for international applicants and late entries.

Full details of the BMAT exam are found on their website and have not been included here due to their likely irrelevance to most readers. However, we have included some tips on preparation, which are useful to candidates of the UKCAT and GAMSAT.

Preparation for BMAT

As for any other entrance exam, practice is the key to being successful.

- The first place to start is at: http://www.bmat.org.uk.

  This has practice questions, provides mark schemes for essays, including the rationale behind answering questions. Their suggested reading materials deal mostly with the theory behind BMAT.

- The official BMAT guide – 'Preparing for BMAT', is an excellent resource, providing questions and worked answers.

- BMAT and UKCAT Uncovered: A guide to medical school entrance exams by T. O. Osinowo, R. A. Weerakkody & H. W. Woodward

- Passing the UK Clinical Aptitude Test and BMAT by Rosalie Hutton, Glenn Hutton, Felicity Walker also has a section on BMAT.

- See the suggested reading for critical thinking listed in the GAMSAT section.

- GCSE revision books are ideal for section 2.

- You should be able to find essay titles online and in forums.

- Keeping abreast of current medical issues, ethics and developments will provide you with examples in your essay, and should be useful for interviews.

- Make your handwriting neater if this is a problem for you.

- UCL have practice questions for Sections 1 & 2, available on: http://www.ucl.ac.uk/lapt/bmat.htm

- It is worth looking for questions through a search engine.

Practice is key for success, including for the essays. Practice the UKCAT papers also, and GAMSAT sections 1 and 2.

Hints and Tips for BMAT

- There is no negative marking in this exam; don't leave blanks.
- Familiarise yourself with the computer marked paper on the official website.
- Write clearly, and erase any wrong answers for sections 1 & 2. If you do not do so, then the computer will interpret your response, and your half rubbed out response, as a failure to answer the question properly, and give you nothing.
- If you are guessing, eliminate any clearly wrong answers to improve your odds of success
- Some people find it easier to read questions before the information provided, since it can mean that you use the time more efficiently, and filter out redundant information
- You are allowed to do workings on your question paper, and doing so may make it easier should you need to come back to a question later on.
- Keep Section 3 relevant.
- Keep it neat.
- Concentrate on your own performance, not anybody else's.
- Immediately after the BMAT exam, make a note of your essay subject and outline its content, as you may be required to discuss that essay at interview.

MSAT

The Medical School Admissions Test (MSAT) is no longer being used. Those schools which did use it (namely King's College London, Queen Mary's and Warwick University), now use the UKCAT exam.

General tips for MCQs and EMQs

- Consider reading the questions prior to the passage.
- Know exactly how long you have per question and stick to it.
- E.g. you have about 1.5min/question for GAMSAT science.
- Star questions you feel you would like to revisit, but still answer (guess) as it is unlikely that you will get back to them.
- Excluding wrong answers can help.
- The information needed to answer is usually provided.
- The questions may occasionally be based on very abstract things. Do not panic, and think about the principles being drawn on.
- Jot down or highlight the key information given in the question.

Commercial Preparation Courses

Some candidates have been successful in the GAMSAT exam on second and even third attempts, simply through perseverance and greater preparation. In addition to private study, taught options include night school and preparation courses with private companies. It is a reasonable argument made by some schools that graduates seeking a place on a highly self-directed graduate medicine course should be more than capable of self-directing their study for the purposes of the entrance exams. But graduates are also mature adults who are capable of choosing which resources work well for them and who realise that good teaching and extra practice can greatly support private study. Remember that there is no association between private companies and the schools or examining boards, so schools can neither endorse nor criticise any commercial options. Many students on graduate medical courses today have found commercial products and services to be invaluable. Many contributors to this book successfully prepared with Dr Prep Ltd (www.drprep.net)

General Exam Tips

The night before the exam:
- Chill out and get a good night's sleep.
- Make sure you have everything ready (see below).
- Make sure you know where you are going, that you have a map, and that you know whether the public transport is working. The author of this chapter once had to hitchhike to a university interview because the train was cancelled.

Useful items to take to the exams.
- Passport or photo driving licence as required – originals +/- photocopies
- Admission ticket/letter.
- Map of how to get there. Allow time for travel problems.
- Limit your valuables – security has been variable
- Ear plugs
- Calculator – but not for BMAT
- Umbrella – people have had to queue in the rain in the past
- Additional clothes - temperature control is tricky in large halls.
- Tissues
- Pens, pencil, ruler - to underline your essay titles
- Sugary sweets & water
- Lunch for those sitting GAMSAT
- Do not make firm arrangements for the evening – GAMSAT over-ran by 2 hours one year
- Being assessed is often challenging and you should expect to feel fairly stretched by the end of the assessment.
- Try not to let other participants intimidate you.

The Interview

The interview is your chance to impress the selectors with your qualities that cannot easily be scored or quantified on paper. As such, we will discuss here not only final preparation and practice, but also the concepts, attitudes and experiences which you should have dwelt on in the months, if not years, preceding the interview.

You will often hear, not least from the medical schools, that preparing for interview can be a risky activity. Preparation is a broad term which covers everything from work experience to practicing answers. Good preparation allows you to express your personal qualities. The concern of admissions tutors does not relate so much to preparation as to 'coaching'. Preparation and practice is undertaken by successful candidates, whilst coaching can be counterproductive, and copying other people's answers will not make you stand out. Candidates are often scored down for stereotyped answers. Coaching implies that candidates are primed with 'correct' answers. There is hardly ever a single correct answer, regurgitation is rarely endearing, and coached candidates may not have the skills to answer a question for which they were not coached.

We encourage preparation and practice and will not provide you with any supposed 'correct' answers.

What are the schools looking for?

Graduate candidates, particularly, should be focused on the fact that they are applying for a career, not just a degree. After all, the interviewers are looking for potential doctors rather than just medical students.

It is worth thinking about why some universities use interviews as part of the selection process. They are an opportunity for you to 'flesh out' your application. Up to that point, you are just a name and number on a list of applicants. The combination of written application, exam and interview maximises the chance for you to let everyone know what a good candidate you are.

The numerous qualities that are sought in potential doctors are highlighted in *Tomorrow's Doctors* and in the medical school prospectuses. Throughout this book, and particularly in chapters 2, 6 and 7, many qualities are discussed which you might hope to demonstrate at interview. You may find it useful to revisit those chapters now.

To name but a few, these qualities include:

Genuine interest in Medicine
- Commitment to medicine
- Motivation towards a medical career
- Realistic view of the role of a doctor
- Appreciation of the medical school's course design

Personal attributes
- Communication (written, listening and speaking)
- Communication with people of different backgrounds
- Communication of difficult information
- Broad social, cultural or sporting interests

- A well-rounded personality
- Empathy, compassion and patience
- Caring attitude and concern for the welfare of others
- Non judgemental
- Interest in People
- A respect for people and their rights, dignity and opinions
- Integrity
- What you can offer the medical school
- Ability to self-criticise and know one's strengths and weakness
- Humility and an open mind

Skills

- Academic knowledge
- Willingness to keep updated
- Ability to describe and discuss important issues in medicine
- Capacity for self-directed knowledge acquisition
- Willingness to accept responsibility
- Practical Skills
- Ability to learn and implement new ideas and skills
- Organisational skills
- Non-academic accomplishments
- Problem-solving skills

Team player

- Recognition of other health professionals' roles
- Teamwork
- Leadership

Coping under stress

- Recognition of the stresses in medicine
- Recognition of stress in oneself and others
- Ability to recognise limitations
- Strategies for coping

You might now be eager to know how to demonstrate the above qualities at interview, but the practicalities of how you will do this will in part vary on the structure and aim of your interview.

Types of Interview Structure
- *Structured*

Structured interview means that all candidates should be asked the exactly the same questions. This means that your interviewers should not ask questions that follow naturally from your first response. This lack of verbal feedback, and often of non verbal feedback can feel unnerving, however the reason for this is to be as fair as possible by giving each candidate the same interview experience and a more objective scoring system. This means that they cannot use your personal statement, as questions derived from it would be unique to you.

Since your answers cannot be debated or prompted you should strive to answer questions fully by giving examples and offering alternative points of view. At most they will ask 'Anything else?' Remember that this does not mean that there should be anything else, it is simply their way of checking that you are ready to move on.

- *Semi - Structured*

Most interviews are semi-structured. The bulk of questions will be prepared in advance but with leeway to develop some questions further. They could include references to your personal statement. Though this format feels less daunting than strictly structured interviews, it does mean that your answers can be debated so be careful not to contradict yourself or your personal statement. Do not assume that there will be a prompting question and only give half an answer. Answer as fully as possible, including giving examples and evidence to support your response.

- *Unstructured*

In a completely unstructured interview, the questions are relatively, or totally, unprepared. They may include similar questions to those offered in structured interviews, or questions developed from your personal statement, or they may follow a completely tortuous and random route. Bear in mind that all the interviewers are likely to be looking for the same skills and attributes, so prepare as much as you can, and consider the arguments to your responses.

- *Selection Centres*

Used by Warwick and Queen Mary's, these centres include a written exercise, the viewing of a taped consultation, a teamwork exercise and completion of a questionnaire. How to deal with video critique and teamwork exercises is dealt with later in this chapter.

- *Multiple Mini Interview System*

Used by King's, and under consideration by St George's, interviewees circulate around eight 5 minute stations. At each station, candidates meet one or two interviewers who ask structured questions, and mark independently. Stations are likely to include scenarios and ethical dilemmas.

- *Availability of your UCAS form to the interviewers*

This generally relates to how structured the interview is. If the interviewers are asking everyone the same question it is impossible to ask something that relates to your personal statement or exam results. For some interviews, the interviewers are blinded to your personal statement and UCAS information. This means that the interviewer knows absolutely nothing about you. You must work into your interview anything that you feel they should know, irrespective of how eloquently you described it in your personal statement. Even for those schools that will read your personal statement, you should bear in mind that it is unlikely to be read in detail. You would be well-advised to divulge at interview that valuable information found within your personal statement, and expand on it. Kings, Nottingham and St George's interviewers will not know your UKCAT/GAMSAT result nor have access to your personal statement. They are essentially blind to your application thus far.

Outline of each school's style of graduate entry medicine interview

The following is a summary of what each graduate medical school is looking for at interview and the structure of the interview. The information has been summarised from communication with each University and their own websites. While there are common skills that they are looking for and the preparation for each kind of interview will be the same, it is worth noting what each university feels is important enough to put in their literature. Tips on how to deal with each kind of interview are included. We then deal with tips which are common to all medical school interviews.

Barts and the London, Queen Mary's School of Medicine and Dentistry and Warwick

GEP medicine interviews for the schools above are conducted jointly. Applicants who apply to both institutes will only need to attend one interview. The interviews are carried out in assessment centre formats and you must prepare to be there for the whole day. They normally include a written exercise based on your ability to reason and prioritise tasks, watching a video and being able to critically analyze it followed by a structured 1:1 interview and finally a group team work exercise watched by a panel of assessors (see later). The medical schools change their format each year so concentrate on what qualities they are trying to investigate by using these tools rather that how the process operates.

They are looking for students who are able to:
- Empathise with patients
- Communicate effectively in a wide range of situations
- Treat others in a caring manner
- Work well as part of a team
- Organise and problem solve
- Show initiative and resilience
- Develop self-directed learning styles

They also expect you to have investigated whether you have these qualities by acquiring significant work experience.

Birmingham

They are looking for academic excellence, demonstration of being well-motivated towards a career in medicine and possession of qualities required of a potential doctor. Their interview is semi-structured, and they may include reference to your personal statement. Answer as fully as possible, including giving examples and evidence to support your response.

Bristol

These are also semi-structured. The interviews last for 15 to 20 minutes and are conducted by two interviewers. You will be asked questions such as why do you want to study medicine, what you know about the course and career and what recent developments in medicine you have read about.

Criteria for assessing the candidate's performance at interview are:

a)   reasons for wanting to study medicine.

b)   awareness of current developments.

c)   ability to communicate.

d)   self-confidence.

e)   enthusiasm.

f)   determination to study.

g)   ability to cope with stress.

h)   how informed is the candidate about the course and career?

i)   overall impression created by candidate.

Each criterion is assessed on a four-point scale. The interviewers complete an "interview proforma" for each candidate. The top-rated interviewees will be made an offer of a place.

Cambridge

Typically you will have interviews of 20-30 minutes; they are structured but informal in nature. As the interviews are based upon the discussion of complex issues, they involve a fair degree of prompting. Don't worry if you are being prompted, this may just mean that you are making progress in the discussion. You are encouraged to read around the subject of medicine. You need to know why you want to study medicine and why at Cambridge, to know about major developments in medicine and demonstrate that you have done some research to find out what the career involves. You may be asked about interests or experiences that you have mentioned in your application.

Put generally the characteristics they are looking for are:

- A passion for medicine
- An ability to think independently, critically and analytically
- Enthusiasm for complex and challenging ideas, intellectual flexibility
- Professional commitment

The interviewers may do this by engaging you in an ethical dilemma (see later).

Imperial

Normally interview panels consist of a chairperson, two members of the selection panel and frequently a lay observer. The interview is not intended to be an intimidating experience and staff will try to put candidates at ease while evaluating the following:

- motivation and realistic approach to medicine and the role of a clinician scientist as a career
- capacity to deal with stress
- evidence of working as both a leader and a team member
- ability to multi-task
- likely contribution to university life
- communication skills, and maturity of character
- understanding of mammalian cell biology
- an ability to think logically and draw conclusions from data

Keele

The interview itself is a formal though friendly process. Each interview lasts exactly 20 minutes and the panel comprises 3 interviewers and a chairman, the majority of whom are practising clinicians. The candidate will not have the opportunity to ask questions of the interviewers or chairman but may raise any questions during the remainder of the day.

The interview is not a test of candidates' academic knowledge.

1) the UCAS personal statement will be used in selecting candidates for interview;

2) interviewers will be blind to exam results and the personal statement, with the exception of the panel chair;

3) ethical dilemmas/clinical scenarios will be used in the interview;

4) the remainder of the interview will be a structured series of questions.

The interview panel, in addition to forming an overall impression of the student, will be assessing in particular the following areas:

- Ability to communicate.
- Why does candidate wish to be a doctor?
- Does the student have genuine outside interests?
- Previous caring experience.
- Matters of a "medical interest".

King's College London

King's have adopted the Multiple Mini Interview (MMI) system. Interviewees circulate from one timed 'station' to another. At each station the candidate will meet one or two interviewers who will ask structured questions and mark the response to the questions independently. Some of the stations have access to the candidates UCAS application form. MMI is similar in style (but not content) to the short objective structures clinical examinations (OSCE) used in medical school assessment.

Leicester

The interview lasts about 15 minutes and is with a senior academic or doctor and a 5th year medical student, both of whom have received training in interviewing. You may be asked to tackle a clinical scenario/ethical dilemma as part of your interview (see later)

The interview is structured and a range of topics may be covered, including ethical issues in medicine, your work experience, recreational activities and so on. The interviewers will be judging your communication abilities, motivation and general suitability to medicine.

Liverpool

Candidates are interviewed for 25 minutes by two people, taken from a panel of academic members of staff (clinical and non-clinical), NHS clinicians, local GPs and members of NHS trusts. It is a semi-structured interview.

Newcastle   .

The interview is conducted by two selectors. The purpose of the interview is to confirm whether the candidate has the aptitude, motivation and personal qualities to succeed as a medical student and as a doctor of the future. The applicant will be graded for evidence of commitment to caring for others, team working with leadership skills, non academic personal interests and insight into medicine as a career with an understanding of the NHS. As the first year of the course is accelerated they are looking for evidence of an aptitude for intensive self-directed study.

Nottingham and St George's

The interview is conducted by a panel of three trained interviewers: a clinician, an academic and a lay person. The interviews are structured, the interviewers will use standardized questions and common criteria and scoring scales and there should be no feedback within the interview or prompting. The questions are based on the following themes:

- Are you realistic about what it means to be a doctor?
- Your interest in the field of medicine

- Your personal attributes necessary for the study and practice of medicine

Medical students are expected to have good communication and listening skills, an understanding of professional issues such as teamwork and respect for the contribution of other professions.

The amount and quality of your work experience will also be assessed as will how reflective you are about what you have learned from this experience.

You will scored as follows:

1 – Someone who did not to answer the question at all or provided no evidence/ detail of previous work or volunteering experience or may be indifferent to the need to have done some type of work experience.
2 – Someone who may have shadowed a GP or hospital doctor for a few days/ weeks or a member of their family who is a healthcare professional
3 – Someone who has taken the initiative to find out what a career in medicine is really all about but there is no obvious consistency to the experiences or perhaps these were in the past or someone who has cared for a sick relative or they themselves have been a patient in hospital
4 - A consistent range of experiences gained over a period up to a year or the candidate may work in the NHS in a clinical setting
5 - More than a year part-time volunteer work in a variety of posts with some relevance to medicine or social care/ special needs education or more than two years full-time in a profession allied to medicine.

St George's prefer work experience to be in a clinical or healthcare setting with access to real patients or those in need of care rather than in a research or corporate setting. It is extremely rare for St George's to offer a place to someone who scores below 3 for work experience, despite the quality of the GAMSAT score and the rest of the interview.

Interviewers will not have your UCAS form, will not be aware of your score in the GAMSAT or of your class of degree.

Oxford

Important selection criteria are:

- academic ability, evidence of originality of thought or initiative
- commitment to medicine
- personal suitability for medicine and the four year course

The exact structure of the interviews will vary from college to college. Some tutors will ask applicants to a brief meeting before the interviews begin. Here the will tell you how the interviews will be conducted and perhaps offer a few words of advice. Interviews are fairly unstructured but will probably include factual questions. The interviewers will be blind to your UKCAT score, but not your personal statement

They may ask you questions to which you do not know the answer. This is done with a view to finding out whether you can think your way through a problem to which you have not been taught the specific answers. An ethical dilemma/clinical scenario may form part of the interview (see later)

St George's

See Nottingham, above.

Southampton

Graduate applicants are not normally interviewed unless the selectors require further information in order to consider the application

University of Wales, Swansea

Interviews will be conducted by panels of trained interviewers and will normally include a non-clinical academic and a medically qualified academic member of University or NHS Trust staff.

The interview will be structured to ascertain your personal attributes qualities and motivation. These will include:

- Understanding the demands of, and commitment to, a career in medicine
- Evidence of and potential for high academic achievement
- A caring and committed attitude towards people
- The ability to communicate effectively
- A willingness to accept responsibility
- Evidence of team working and broad, social, cultural or sporting interests
- Ability to describe and discuss important issues in medicine

Warwick

See Barts, above.

General Tips for approaching Graduate Entry Interviews

Tidy up your thoughts

It is useful to think of your personal experiences and write down examples of when you have demonstrated the different qualities that the universities are looking for. You might find it useful to create a table with the common qualities required and examples of your experiences.

For each of the main qualities listed on the second and third pages of this chapter (and any further identified by your chosen school), create a table as shown below. Just as you would when filling in an application form for a job, make sure that you have examples that match all aspects of the 'job description'. Your best experience is often applicable to more than one of the qualities, but it is useful to have different examples for each so that you don't have to use the same experience twice. Doing this written exercise will enable you to recall useful experiences in the pressure of the moment. For example:

Communication 1	
Situation	When working in the hospice, talking with a patient that had a hearing difficulty
Action	At first just spoke louder and slower - didn't work very well and disturbed other patients. Found out from patient if it was a long standing problem and if they had a hearing aid. They did, made sure it was working and had a battery in it and made sure patient was wearing it when we needed to communicate. Asked them what the best way of communicating with them was Looked up best ways of communicating on the Royal Association for Deaf people website
Result	Improved communication and written advice for all staff on how the patient liked to communicate
Reflection	First action was instinctive but not very effective. Best way of solving the problem was to involve patient. Will remember this when dealing with patients as a medical student and doctor

Communication 2	
Situation	When shadowing a GP in her clinic, GP explaining test results to a patient
Action	GP found out what the patients concerns were and what they knew already and what they wanted to know. Then told patient what the test results were and explained the interpretation without jargon. Checked the patient understood in a non patronising way. Explained what the next steps would be, involving the patient in the choice. Summarised the information again at the end. Gave time for patient to ask questions and interrupt.
Result	Patient upset at results but grateful to doctor for clear and supportive explanation
Reflection	I started to understand the aspects of good communication and how this can help make consultations a less distressing experience for the patient.

Practice discussing each of the required skills out loud and to anyone that will listen. Discuss why the skills are important. Do you have these skills? What is your evidence?

How to answer a question!

Think about how you would like to hear a doctor respond to a question. What would inspire confidence and trust? This is what the interviewers are looking for. We will consider three aspects to help you present your response. Firstly, your form – here we mean the nature and quality of your speech as well as body language. Secondly, your structure – flow and categorisation. Thirdly, your content – the importance of comments that are accurate, relevant and supported with evidence.

Form

This is the hardest of the three aspects for you to analyse and even harder to correct. It is also fundamentally important. If you are inaudible, or sit and giggle, you will struggle to compete.

The key here is to practice and get feedback. Everyone's opinion of your performance is valid – are you making sense? Does your practice interviewer visualise someone like you advising them on their medical care? For the first time, pay attention to your mother – if she has always scolded you for running your hands through your hair, now is the time to consider that she might be right. Similarly, do not only seek advice from those people you are sure will give you only positive feedback, seek criticism too. The best person to approach is probably the one you are most embarrassed to ask! Ask a medical person to give you a practice interview. Some people choose to go to interview practice courses.

Structure

Rather like the structure of an essay, consider giving an introduction outlining what you are about to say, followed by your evidence and then a conclusion to finish your answer. Give a full response, when answering a question that requires an example of your experiences, reflect on them, what you learnt and what you might do differently next time, signposting at each change of subject.

How often have you thought, or said, "that came out wrong"? Or confused a friend because you had changed subject without indicating that change? Or had to back track, saying "sorry, I should have explained that bit first"? This is an easy area to make big improvements. Think before you start! Pause for longer than feels natural - the gaping pause you feel will not seem as long to the interviewers, who will respect you for thinking about their well-thought-out question. Feel free to say "I will just think about that for a moment." Even if you are not surprised by the question, still pause. It might be subtly different from your immediate assumption.

Many people find it helpful to categorise what they are about to say. 'There are 3 aspects to my answer – X,Y,Z. In terms of X,.......'. Chunking in this way makes your reply easier to follow, and gives you, and the interviewers, a framework in advance. Alternatively, follow the same rules as you were taught for essay writing at school. Give an introduction, evidence (categorisation could equally come in here) and conclusion.

Whenever you give broad headings or a list, by way of an introduction, you should then give examples, particularly in a structured interview. Anyone can state simple things. For instance, all candidates are likely to be able to state that communication is an important skill as a doctor. *You* could *describe* a doctor who has communicated well. Perhaps your doctor really listened to your concerns about your spots when you were a teenager. Or tell of the time when you witnessed sad news being broken well (or badly) to a relative. Or tell of the skills you identified in a doctor you shadowed who was particularly good at communication. This book cannot give you your examples, it can merely suggest that you have them and use them.

Content

Answer the question! If you give a pre-prepared answer to a different question you will score poorly. This may sound obvious, but it is extremely tempting to give your perfectly-rehearsed answer to a surprise question that you have never thought of. Pausing before answering will reduce the risk of this occurring.

Surprise questions may seem nasty but they give you the opportunity to impress the interviewers with your communication skills. Pause, think, chunk your response, be yourself, be honest, and then stop. Do not verbally wander the recesses of your mind for something profound, just answer the question and move on.

Many candidates do themselves a disservice by underselling themselves and missing the opportunity to demonstrate their strengths, or conversely try too hard to 'impress'. The interviewer is not interested in which famous surgeons you have met, but what you have learnt from your experiences. Be proud of your experiences. Cherish them. If you have undertaken work experience, you will have gained an insight into people's lives which is a privilege.

Common Mistakes & things to bear in mind

Speaking too fast
Slowing down will not only help to avoid exhausting your interviewers, you will probably deliver your information more concisely and will automatically improve your structure and content.

Being defensive
Classic examples of this for graduate entry courses are thinking that you are too old and instead of answering "why do you want to study medicine?" the question the older candidate obviously heard was "why do you think you have got enough marbles left to do this, you old fool?" The decision to interview you means that your age does not preclude you

from studying, and that means that lots of very wise, experienced (and old) people have sat around a big table deciding that old folks like you can be just as valuable as the young ones. Of course, older candidates need to show a greater degree of commitment, but that comes from passion, enthusiasm and experience, not a defensive attitude and a biography of your failures.

Similarly, if you are specifically asked at interview why your A-level results are so horribly bad, again, resist the temptation to offer excuses. You might offer something along the lines of, "Well, there were family/personal problems for me at the time but ultimately I did not work hard enough and got the results I deserved." By accepting responsibility, you will have demonstrated maturity, honesty and an ability to develop yourself.

Nervous habits

Interviews know that you will be nervous and really can take it into account, it's very normal. However, whilst you cannot stop yourself from going bright red, you can avoid nail biting, neck scratching, mouth covering, hand wringing, ceiling gazing and nervous laughing. Sit on your hands if necessary.

Interviewers get very nervous too!

Remembering that interviewers are only human might help you to feel less intimidated. One of the author's interviewers later admitted that he was tremendously nervous that he was fundamentally responsible for at least the next year of someone's life.

Not smiling

A fixed smile is horrid, of course, but if you are answering a question in which you are describing your enthusiasm for medicine, a cold, blank face does not help to convince the examiners of that enthusiasm.

Being Arrogant

Some people may give the impression of arrogance by not being able to discuss different points of view. Try to show your understanding of different sides of the argument. Critical analysis does not mean being negative. They are looking for your ability to understand all components of a situation, show empathy to those involved, and make analytical comments. Derogatory comments often reflect more on the people making them. There is always something that you can learn from every situation. Similar, take care with 'certainty' in any ethical dilemma. A dilemma is by definition a complex issue.

Being patronising / too technical

Demonstrate your communication skills by pitching your answers appropriately. You should be introduced at the start of the interview. Try to remember each interviewer's profession; you may even be able to involve them in your answer more: "I imagine you see that sort of thing in your department all the time."

Drawing a blank

You may really draw a complete blank on a question, for instance: "tell us about a time when you have had to take on responsibility." The interviewers are obviously looking for more than just a one sentence example. They are looking for reflection and your understanding of the importance of responsibility within medical practice. So, if you are genuinely at a loss, you might approach it by first apologizing for being unable to recall an example, and then perhaps you may be able to show insight into how a colleague handled responsibility well and why that skill is important in a doctor. You may well think of an example whilst describing these things. Make your answer snappy, indicating your need to move on, and let it go.

It is true that they are not there to catch you out

Equally, do not set yourself up for a fall by (for instance) being arrogant, saying you are interested in something you know nothing about, or saying that you do not like what you are doing at the moment because you do not like needy people.

Do not be fazed by people making notes/scores

It is a fair process for you. And for goodness sake do not try to look at them! You are trying to embark on a career with necessarily high standards of professional conduct – you do not want to look like a cheat. Look at your interviewer instead. Also, seeing the scores will not help you – is the highest score 1 or 10?

Try to get a balance between being over and under prepared

There is an easy solution to being under prepared of course - prepare. If you are over prepared, try to relax, try to feel the emotions that you are describing. You do not want to be describing what a death in your family meant to you with a monotone voice normally saved for shopping list recital.

Try not to be a walking dictionary

Long lists of abbreviations/names of departments/consultants are not impressive. Also, there may be non-medical people on the panel. Remain human and endearing.

Example Questions

The questions here have been picked not necessarily for their frequency of occurrence, but in order to demonstrate common skills applied in such answers.

What makes a good doctor?

The qualities described at the start of this chapter should provide some ideas upon which to build your answer. However, do not simply recite a list – anyone can do that. Your answer should be framed in the light of your work experience and you should have developed your own understanding. If you develop examples from your experiences, you will demonstrate commitment and insight.

Why do you want to change to medicine at this stage?

This question is not: "why have you failed before?", or "aren't you too old?" There is no reason to be defensive. Have respect and appreciation for your current profession, explain how medicine provides additional benefits to you now, view your maturity positively, be realistic but not negative and simply describe your motivation. You should have a positive answer to any question which asks why you want to do something.

Tell us about a particularly stressful time in your life, work or personal, and how you coped with it.

Again, your interviewers are looking for more than a one sentence statement. They are looking for insight, and a demonstration of skills. Explain why the experience is relevant to medicine. Remember that everyone found their first degree stressful; most graduates have something better that they can discuss.

What work and voluntary experience have you had which would help you to become a good doctor and help you in your studies?

Again, do not bore your interviewers with a list. Similarly, do not be showy about whom you have worked with. Also, do not act as though you know everything there is to know about the area of medicine that you witnessed. Being arrogant is not a useful attribute in a doctor. Be humble and enthusiastic, 'paint pictures' of memorable patients (remember to be anonymous) and interesting things that you have witnessed, or skills that you were able to demonstrate.

What pressures do you think doctors face in their professional and personal lives?

Again, this question should be framed in the light of your work experience and you should have developed your own understanding and insight. Pressures that you may have witnessed, and can expand on, might include: hard work (as a student or doctor), hours worked, uncooperative/ungrateful patients, difficult colleagues, death and suffering, management and political pressures (e.g. rationing), safety, relationship pressures, an increasingly litigious society, etc.

Explain a time when you have had to communicate difficult information.

With this type of question, do try to pick a good example. We have actually heard one candidate describe how difficult it was to communicate some rather sensitive information in a text message. Demonstrate that you recognise what is good communication and why it is important for a doctor to communicate well. Be humble and acknowledge what you learnt from the experience and what you could have done differently.

Current Affairs and Advances in Medicine

You may be asked if there is anything of a medical nature that has interested you in the news lately. It is not useful for us to attempt to summarise current affairs here. You should have a broad understanding of many topics in health, science, finance, politics and ethics relating to healthcare, and a more detailed understanding of a few issues. Websites at the end of this chapter will be a great source of further reading, in addition to an overview of information in the newspapers – which is of course what patients read. Try to think about the different aspects of what you read – what does your topic mean to patients, relatives, doctors, NHS finances, public health, ethics and so on. Think about the importance of your chosen topic(s) to different groups and read about media topics from different perspectives, from *The Sun* to *Nature*.

Asking Questions of the Interviewer

An interviewer will often conclude the interview by inviting you to ask any questions. This is not an indication that you ought to, or that they feel you should say something now that you did not say earlier. They are courteously providing you with an opportunity to ask a specific question, should you have one, and nothing else. Do not see it as an opportunity to give yourself more time and another opportunity to engage the interviewers in new detail. If you ask a question, do not ask for information that is available in the prospectuses or should have been obtained prior to application. They will have another interview to do after you, and would probably rather get on with it, so avoid unnecessary questions. Whether you ask a question or not, always thank the interviewer(s) for their time.

A note about clothes

Your personality should be expressed in your answers, not your clothes and accessories. Interviewers are tired and often bored people, so it is easy for them to be distracted, indeed mesmerized, by a piece of bling or interesting hair style and fail to listen to much said.

Men; wear a suit and tie. Polish your shoes. Avoid overly styled hair.

Ladies, wear a suit or similar. Polish your shoes. Skirts should not expose your thigh when standing. Remove all but the most subtle jewelry, and tie your hair back. Make up should be subtle.

Ethical Dilemmas/Clinical Scenarios

A discussion in which you think through problems or issues, explain or justify your position and think for yourself, is a marvelous way to test many skills. Some schools give you time to prepare in advance of the interview, whilst others may simply include a question within the interview. At what point an interview question becomes 'an ethical dilemma' is subjective, and you would be wise to prepare for any school. Schools we believe are more likely to enter into this sort of discussion are Cambridge, Keele, King's, Leicester, Oxford, Queens and Warwick. Schools will look for realism and a balanced outlook. You will probably have a gut reaction and a sense of what is right, but try to see different points of view and potential flaws in your argument. Whilst offering your opinion will inform the interviewers of your outlook, an empathy for different views is useful, not least because your opinion could be deemed wrong.

You may be pushed until your knowledge and ideas are exhausted. This does not mean that the interviewers do not like you. Indeed, it could mean that they are enjoying the discussion with you. Equally, do not become argumentative when pushed. As a doctor, you would have to remain calm and professional, to listen to the views of others, and be willing to accommodate those views.

While admitting that this book is not the forum to go into a detailed discussion of ethics it is perhaps worth mentioning one of the frameworks for thinking about ethics, i.e. the four principles

- Respect for autonomy: respecting the decision-making capacities of autonomous persons; enabling individuals to make reasoned informed choices.
- Beneficence: this considers the balancing of benefits of treatment against the risks and costs; the healthcare professional should act in a way that benefits the patient.
- Non maleficence: avoiding the causation of harm; the healthcare professional should not harm the patient. All treatment involves some harm, even if minimal, but the harm should not be disproportionate to the benefits of treatment.
- Justice: distributing benefits, risks and costs fairly; the notion that patients in similar positions should be treated in a similar manner.

This is just one of many frameworks to prompt ethical debate when thinking about medical issues. It is useful to do some background reading as it may help you to structure your answer in interview.

Consider the following scenario:
A 15 year old girl undergoes an emergency operation for the removal of an ectopic pregnancy (a dangerous pregnancy outside the womb). She asks you not to tell her mother anything. The mother demands to know what has happened to her daughter.

You may or may not know the current requirements relating to confidentiality, and it does not matter - the interviewer is likely to be most interested in how laterally you are able to think and how well you are able to structure and present your response.

The notes below are not prescriptive or exhaustive, but simply ideas that one might consider developing in an answer.

- Identify that this is a dilemma about confidentiality
- Identify that the girl is a patient
- Identify that the patient is a minor
- Is this statutory rape?
- Who is the father?
- Consider when it might be appropriate to disclose patient information
- Should the mother be informed?
- Should the police be informed?
- This will lead you to your dilemma
- a patient is owed a duty of confidentiality – it is the very essence of the patient/doctor relationship
- is a mother allowed information regarding her daughter's medical care when that daughter is below a certain age?
- If you know about confidentiality, competence (especially Gillick/Fraser), consent and disclosure you can offer more evidence about what should be considered – do not worry if you do not know about these things, you will learn about them at medical school!
- It is likely that you will not know the precise answer to your dilemma; otherwise it would not be a very good dilemma! So, debate the issue and offer your own personal opinion in a non-judgemental way.

- It can be a nice conclusion to say that whilst you have offered your personal opinion, that you understand that you will be working within guidelines that may not always meet with your own personal opinion.

(For more information, see www.gmc-uk.org/standards and follow the links to guidance and confidentiality and in particular sections 36-39. You might also follow the links to consent and children (section 23). It is an excellent site to gain a broad understanding of many ethico-legal issues.)

Video Critique

Queen Mary's and Warwick , as part of the assessment centre, may ask you to watch a ten minute video, in which you may be able to make notes. The video may relate to, for instance, a GP consultation. They are mostly testing your understanding of communication skills. Think about what the doctor does well, and less well. If you think that the doctor has done something poorly, try to empathise with why that might have happen. Do the same with the patient. Consider, for both doctor and patient

- Introduction
- Listening skills
- Speaking skills
- Any written communication (or absence of it)
- Body language
- The set up of the room
- Any issues with consent, confidentiality etc
- Closure of the consultation

Team Work Tips

Queen Mary's and Warwick , as part of the assessment centre, may ask that you undertake a group task, such as a case study, where your performance in the group will be assessed. Please note that medical schools change their format each year and the selection centre this year will almost certainly use different tools to this. Try not to think so much about the details of *how* the selection centre operates, but rather *why* you are asked to do these things. Put yourself in the interviewers' shoes. The selection centres are just another way of testing the same skills that we discussed elsewhere.

Here are some tips to help you to perform well, taken from
www.kent.ac.uk/careers/sk/teamwork.htm

- When given the information for a group exercise, underline key points and the likely arguments and counter arguments. Look for any red herrings (irrelevant or misleading facts).
- Try to be yourself. Don't try to put on a façade or mask.
- Talk to the other candidates and assessors between exercises to help keep yourself relaxed.
- Keep a note of the finish time. Don't allow the group to over-run. Statements like *"look we only have 5 minutes left so we need to get a move on"* may help.
- For some exercises it helps to decide on the criteria on which you will make your choices and then stick to this. E.g. if you have to decide who to save from a sinking ship do you save the youngest, fittest or ones with useful skills? Spend time in preparation and planning rather than just jumping in - decide your objectives and priorities, but don't take too long.

- If a particular group member is quiet try to get them to contribute. It's a good idea to encourage them along the lines *"We haven't heard from Mike yet; what do you think?"*

- Voting for a particular choice is a last resort and should only be used if persuasion and consensus have failed and time is running out.

- Stick up for your opinions and argue persuasively and with logic for them, but also listen to the opinions of others and support those you agree with. Don't belittle the ideas of others - in most cases you're not competing directly against the other members of the group - everyone could be selected or everyone rejected.

- Go for quality rather than quality in your contributions. Don't talk aimlessly. Try to move the group forward by your contributions e.g. *"Look this is not going anywhere. Why don't we move on and come back to this topic later"*

- Summarising can sometimes help to clarify the position. *"Before we go on shall I summarise what we've agreed"*

- If a dominant individual tries to "hijack" the group, don't be afraid to challenge them, but do this calmly, logically and diplomatically, not by attacking them. You could ask *"What are your reasons for saying that?"*

- If you are made leader of an exercise it's a good idea to ask for volunteers for particular tasks such as note taking and to delegate responsibility. Identify the strengths of the other group members and use them. Don't get too involved in the fine detail of the task - your role as the leader is to keep an overview.

- Keep cool and use your sense of humour. Be assertive, tactful and persuasive and work with the group. Listen to what everyone has to say. Don't interrupt or put down other group members.

- Try to be creative - introduce new ideas or build on the ideas of others.

- See www.kent.ac.uk/careers/sk/teamwork.htm for more

Your aim is to inspire confidence in your ability to succeed in medical school and to become a compassionate and skilled physician. It is important to communicate why you believe you are a qualified candidate and what you have done to prepare for medical school.

Further help

- www.bma.org
- www.thelancet.com
- www.gmc-uk.org
- www.bmj.com
- www.studentbmj.com
- www.who.int
- www.direct.gov.uk
- www.nejm.org

Two months before the interview

- Don't wait until your interview invitation letter to start preparing.
- Find out when your universities hold their interviews
- Book out these days in your diary.
- If you are working, warn employers that you may need a day off with only 1-2 week's notice.
- Start filling in your qualities chart
- Practice answering some of the common questions
- Get a friend to ask you questions and video your replies
- Watch the video, reflect on your own and your friend's impressions and make any changes necessary
- Research the university and the course by reading the prospectus, by going on open days and speaking to current students
- Reflect on what you have learnt about medicine during your work experience, what does it mean to you?

When you get your invitation letter

- Reply promptly
- Read the letter closely and get together any supporting documentation that is requested
- Make copies of any certificates

2 weeks before the interview

- Get your interview clothing ready. Put it on and make sure it fits and is appropriate. Get it cleaned.
- Arrange transport, i.e. book train tickets.
- Print out a map of the area that you are travelling to.
- Consider making a dummy run.
- Carry out another practice interview with a friend or colleague, bearing in mind the changes you decided on after your first practice.

Day before the interview

- Prepare your clothes
- Collect certificates and other documentation in a file
- Check time and place of interview again, have your map ready
- Check for any traffic/public transport problems (including London underground where applicable) so you can leave extra time on the day if necessary.

The day of the interview

- Take a map with you
- Take your invitation letter and contact details.
- Check that you have all the documentation that the university has requested. For example, your original degree certificate, photo identification and criminal records bureau application.
- Arrive at least 30 minutes before the interview time. Be aware that it may take some time to find the right building on a large campus.
- Relax before the interview by walking around the block or carrying out breathing exercises.

The interview

- Be friendly and polite with everyone you meet.
- Greet interviewer in confident, professional, friendly manner.
- Answer questions in a positive tone of voice.
- Have good body language; attentive & listening, formal but relaxed.
- Let your personality come across.

After The interview

- Jot down a few notes about the interview including questions that went well or not so well to help you at your next interview
- Continue to behave professionally and quietly until you are far away from the building.

And Finally

We hope that this book will help you to secure a place at medical school. We wish you the best of luck in your studies and look forward to meeting some of you during your training. However, the sad fact is that most applicants will not secure a place. Whilst it would not be appropriate for some candidates in particular to be awarded a place at medical school, many unsuccessful applicants have great potential and may well succeed on subsequent attempts. Some of the best graduate entry medical students that we have encountered admitted to having applied in three consecutive years before receiving an offer.

Age not withstanding, you might consider treating your unsuccessful applications as a learning opportunity. You will have undertaken some, if not all, of the following: work experience, the completion of application forms, preparation for and completion of entrance exams and interviews. This experience is enormously valuable – try to remember how daunted and uninformed you were when you started this process.

Above all, learn from your mistakes. Could you have started work experience sooner? Could you have found more valuable work experience? Did you get the most out of that work experience? Were you able to think deeply about patients, the pros and cons of medicine, and about yourself? Did you prepare adequately for the exams? Did you practise all the sample papers? Did you practise writing timed essays? Did anyone feed back to you on the standard of those essays? Did you frequently verbalise your medical aspirations and gain feedback on whether your desire and insight was apparent?

Few candidates prepare as well as they could, including the successful ones. If you have been through the process once, you have an advantage over the candidate who is navigating their way for the first time. Of course, we hope that this book goes a long way to ensuring that candidates do not feel lost in their application year, or indeed as they embark upon their training and beyond.

There are options for studying medicine other than graduate entry, of course. You may consider a standard entry course, an overseas course, a foundation programme or an access to medicine course. These options are distinct from graduate entry and will therefore not be discussed here. However, if you feel that you have exhausted your efforts in applying to graduate entry courses, you may find that there are other options available to you.

We wish you all the best in the pursuit of your vocation.